VISION

Biophysics and Biochemistry of the Retinal Photoreceptors

Publication Number 622
AMERICAN LECTURE SERIES®

A Monograph in
The BANNERSTONE DIVISION *of*
AMERICAN LECTURES IN LIVING CHEMISTRY

Edited by
I. NEWTON KUGELMASS, M.D., Ph.D., Sc.D
Consultant to the Departments of Health and Hospitals
New York, New York

VISION

Biophysics and Biochemistry of the
Retinal Photoreceptors

By

JEROME J. WOLKEN, Ph.D.

Professor of Biophysics
Head, Department of Biological Sciences
and Biophysical Research Laboratory
Carnegie Institute of Technology
Pittsburgh, Pennsylvania

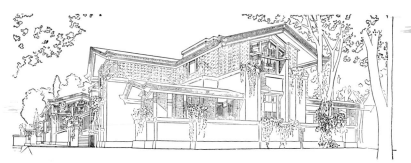

CHARLES C THOMAS • **PUBLISHER**
Springfield • *Illinois* • *U. S. A.*

Published and Distributed Throughout the World by
CHARLES C THOMAS • PUBLISHER
BANNERSTONE HOUSE
301-327 East Lawrence Avenue, Springfield, Illinois, U.S.A.
NATCHEZ PLANTATION HOUSE
735 North Atlantic Boulevard, Fort Lauderdale, Florida, U.S.A.

With THOMAS BOOKS careful attention is given to all details of manufacturing and design. It is the Publisher's desire to present books that are satisfactory as to their physical qualities and artistic possibilities and appropriate for their particular use. THOMAS BOOKS will be true to those laws of quality that assure a good name and good will.

Printed in the United States of America
H-2

THIS BOOK IS DEDICATED TO

Ann, Jonathan, Johanna, and Erik

FOREWORD

Our Living Chemistry Series was conceived by editor and publisher to advance the newer knowledge of chemical medicine in the cause of clinical practice. The interdependence of chemistry and medicine is so great that physicians are turning to chemistry, and chemists to medicine in order to understand the underlying basis of life processes in health and disease. Once chemical truths, proofs and convictions become sound foundations for clinical phenomena, key hybrid investigators clarify the bewildering panorama of biochemical progress for application in everyday practice, stimulation of experimental research, and extension of postgraduate instruction. Each of our monographs thus unravels the chemical mechanisms and clinical management of many diseases that have remained relatively static in the minds of medical men for three thousand years. Our new series is charged with the *nisus élan* of chemical wisdom, supreme in choice of international authors, optimal in standards of chemical scholarship, provocative in imagination for experimental research, comprehensive in discussions of scientific medicine, and authoritative in chemical perspective of human disorders.

Dr. Wolken, of Pittsburgh, presents his extensive studies on retinal photoreceptors to elucidate the mechanism of vision. These studies give us an experimental glimpse of how the retinal receptors, the 125 million rods and 7 million cones, function upon light excitation in transmitting signals to the brain in order to produce seeing images of our environment. Many of the fundamental properties of vision are thus vested in the physical and chemical properties of retinal molecules. The story of vision follows the phylogenetic development of the eye and its retina for millions of years from the light-detecting eye spots of protozoa, to the imaging compound eyes of arthropods, to the refracting eyes of vertebrates including man. The process that begins with action of light on a visual pigment ends in visual sensations.

The visual system involves first the passage of light through the dioptric mechanism of the eye to form images of external objects on the retina. The images are then recorded by photoreceptors with absorption of light by a photosensitive pigment which changes its chemical nature and initiates a nervous discharge in the subsequent neurones of the retina. The nervous discharge forms the message sent over the transmission system of the nerves to the brain giving rise to a sensation of light or color and/or initiation of motor reactions in the body. Thus we have two receiving mechanisms intermingled in the eye and optic nerve—one is the dark-adapted mechanism for night-time and the other, the light-adapted mechanism for daytime and for color appreciation.

The nature of vision has been the subject of speculation for centuries. Pre-Hippocratic philosophers considered vision the result of information gathered by antennae-like rays emitted by the eye that struck on an object and were deflected back to the eye conveying information of the outer world. The fallacious idea had no visual enfolding yet persisted unto the seventeenth century with varying modifications. Two thousand years of thinking about the eye in a totally wrong way serves to underline the importance of the three great concepts which were lacking—the notion of image formation by a lens, the idea of electrical impulses in nerve fibers, the idea of how these impulses give rise to conscious sensation. We know about the first two but little about the third—if there is such a stage.

Vision in dim light with objects appearing colorless, is due to stimulation of the rods, while daylight vision and appreciation of color are due to stimulation of cones. Vision is thus the end result of absorption of light by rods or cones followed by stimulation of neurones in the retina and brain. Examination of what we can see under different conditions reveals how the whole system of light-sensitive cells, retinal neurones and brain can react, while examination of the properties of light-sensitive pigments from the retina gives information about the primary light-catching process. The theory of vision formulated by the author correlates the two sets of data.

Photoreceptors offer advantages over other receptors in the study of sensory mechanisms for in such a study the very first step in the transducer mechanism for translating the stimulus into nervous action is clarified by the author. The basis for visual function is vested in the molecular structure and molecular chemistry identified with all photoreceptor systems. All appear as crystalline-like structures with sufficient surfaces for the photosensitive pigment-complexes $retinene_1$ or $retinene_2$ to be oriented as monolayers in specific molecular configurations for light capture and energy transfer—the critical mechanism for initiating the visual process. Its high degree of perfection enables us to exploit the advantages of luminous energy as a source of information, but its shortcomings set limits to our visual performance. The advancing front of medical science lies in the borderlands between the older sciences. Dr. Wolken explored many fields, learned many skills, and dared to apply to a challenging problem in one area the insight he has gained in studying many. With accurate experiment and observation to work upon, imagination becomes the architect of scientific theory.

> "Let us then be up and doing
> With a heart for any fate,
> Still achieving, still pursuing,
> Learn to labour and to wait."

I. NEWTON KUGELMASS, M.D., PH.D., SC.D., *Editor*

PREFACE

IN A MOMENT of excess enthusiasm and because of the encouragement of Dr. I. Newton Kugelmass, Editor of the series, *American Lectures in Living Chemistry,* I have undertaken in this monograph to summarize my investigations of a small part of a very large subject vision, one of the most highly developed of the special senses of man. How we see—by way of an image impinged on the retina is one of the most intriguing of unsolved biological problems.

There are many large areas of visual exploration: the optics and image formation; the biosynthesis of visual pigments and their photochemistry; the electrophysiology; and the psychophysics. Information in all of these areas is required if we are to understand how photoexcitation upon the retinal photoreceptor cells leads to a picture of our environment; therefore it becomes necessary to know more of the structure of the retinal cells, their chemistry and their physiology. Only then can we make progress towards our understanding nervous excitation and towards the prevention of the blinding diseases of man.

Interest in the problems of vision has developed new and vigorous impetus in the past decade. Many symposia have been held and published and many texts and visual research journals begun. In addition, progress reports on various aspects of vision research have been appearing in a variety of scientific journals.

This monograph is in no way designed to review all of this material, nor to cover all areas of research in vision—areas which cannot be treated comprehensively in a monograph of this type. Therefore it is necessary to give references to major texts and symposia. These include the four volume series, *The Eye,* 1962, edited by Hugh Davson, Academic Press, New York, especially Volume 2, *The Visual Process;* the Symposium on Photoreception, edited by O.V. St. Whitlock and J.J. Wolken, *Ann. New York Acad. Sci., 74*:163-406, 1958; the Caracas Symposium on Mechanisms of Vision, *J. Gen. Physiol., 43,* suppl. 2, 1960; the Freiburg Symposium on *Neurophysiology and Psychophysics of the Visual System,* edited by

R. Jung and H. Kornhuber, Springer, Berlin, 1961; the M.I.T. Symposium on *Sensory Communication,* edited by W.A. Rosenblith, John Wiley, New York, 1961; the Symposium on *Light and Life,* W.D. McElroy and B. Glass, editors, Johns Hopkins University Press, Baltimore, Maryland, 1961; the International Congress of Anatomists, *The Structure of the Eye,* G.K. Smelser, editor, Academic Press, New York, 1961; the Symposium on *Biological Receptor Mechanisms,* J.W.L. Beament, editor, Academic Press, New York, 1962; and the Symposium on *Physiological Optics, J. Opt. Soc. Am., 53,* 1963. Numerous other references may be found within these works as well as within this text.

The present treatment of the text then is a summarization of my own studies; therefore it should not be construed as a textbook but rather as a personal account of experiments that seeks to give an individual approach to research on the photoreceptors of a variety of organisms. This research is an attempt to organize these photoreceptors into a logical structure and thus to understand a part of the visual process. The work was, in a sense, begun more than a decade ago in the laboratories of the Rockefeller Institute, New York, where I was first introduced to the phenomena of photoreception about which I began to raise questions in terms of plant and animal cells. The experiments described here, however, were carried out at the Biophysical Research Laboratory, Eye and Ear Hospital, University of Pittsburgh School of Medicine, Pittsburgh, Pennsylvania. The text also follows in part a series of lectures given while I was a Guest Professor in the Department of Biophysics at Pennsylvania State University, University Park, Pennsylvania, in the Spring of 1963.

This book should be of interest to researchers and clinicians working in the field of eye research. Hopefully, it will also excite students to explore this vast, unknown area of one of the most important of the special senses of man—vision.

Jerome J. Wolken

ACKNOWLEDGMENTS

I WOULD LIKE to thank those who have been associated with these studies in the Biophysical Research Laboratory, especially, Dr. J.M. Bowness, Dr. G.K. Strother, Dr. J.J. van der Gon, I.J. Scheer, G. Gallick, R. Florida, R. Forsberg, K. Kotovsky, Dr. G. Marak, Dr. G. Contis, and all who have worked in the laboratory seeking answers to the visual system of animals.

I would also like to thank the McClintic Foundation and the Stoner Foundation of Pittsburgh, the National Council to Combat Blindness, Inc., New York, New York, and the National Aeronautics and Space Administration, Washington, D. C., for their financial support.

I especially wish to thank the U.S. Public Health Service Institute of Neurological Diseases and Blindness, Bethesda, Maryland, for their continuous support over a decade of this research and for a Career Professorship awarded to me in 1962, University of Pittsburgh School of Medicine.

The actuality of summarizing these experiments and my thoughts into a readable form was carried out in the quiet of the Mellon Institute of Pittsburgh. The photography was done by Mr. Robert Florida, and many of the illustrations and tracings were done by Mr. Gilbert Arnold of the Mellon Institute. My special thanks go to Miss Jane W. Candia for the task of transcribing this work into a readable manscript.

For the encouragement to delve into these problems with maximum freedom, I would like to thank Dr. Murray F. McCaslin, Professor and Head of the Department of Ophthalmology, University of Pittsburgh School of Medicine.

I would like to acknowledge the following journals for permission to reproduce certain figures from my own work published in: *Applied Optics, Biochimica et Biophysica Acta, Journal of Biophysical and Biochemical Cytology, Journal of Cell Biology, Journal of Cellular and Comparative Physiology, Experimental Cell Research, Experimen-*

tal Eye Research, Journal of Experimental Zoology, Journal of General Physiology, Investigative Ophthalmology, Journal of the Optical Society of America, Journal of Protozoology, and the publishers, Academic Press, Inc., New York, New York, and Rutgers University Press, New Brunswick, New Jersey.

J. J. W.

CONTENTS

VISION

Biophysics and Biochemistry of the
Retinal Photoreceptors

Chapter I

INTRODUCTION

IN THE LATTER half of the nineteenth century, experimental biologists began to lay the foundation for the scientific study of sensory physiology. Herman von Helmholtz (1867) was one of the first physiologists to recognize that the sense organs, the receptors for sight, hearing, taste, smell, and touch, are the detectors through which we know the world. His studies on the problems of vision and hearing are now classics in the area of sensory physiology.

Now, however, the clue to the function of the sense organs lies in an understanding of their molecular anatomy, chemistry, and physics. These problems are truly biophysical ones that constitute one of the greatest challenges in biological research since they underlie how organisms react in an integrated fashion as a whole animal.

Light stimulation of living organisms is mediated through photosensitive pigment-complexes within photoreceptor structures. There are three responses: tropisms (photokinesis, phototaxis), bending or swimming to or away from light; photosynthesis, the conversion of light energy to chemical energy in the synthesis of sugars; and vision, the conversion of light energy to chemical energy to electrical energy to initiate a visual image.

Photosensitivity is found throughout nature, from the photoresponses of bacteria, to vision in man. It takes place in a very narrow part of the radiation spectrum, the visible, from 4000 to 8000 Å. Radiation shorter than 3900 Å, the ultraviolet, has profound effects on protoplasm; what part, if any, it plays in the visual processes of vertebrates is not known. However, the invertebrates, such as the insects, have their major spectral response near 3600 Å; therefore they must possess molecules that can absorb this energy.

In these processes, various types of photoreceptors have been identified morphologically and so named to indicate their physical structure and their place in the phylogenetic scheme of development.

[3]

In plant cells, the photoreceptors for photosynthesis are the *chromatophores* of bacteria, the *plastids* of algae, and the *chloroplasts* of higher plants. The *chromatophores* in animal cells are not to be confused with the photosynthetic chromatophores of bacteria, although they contain colored pigments (e.g., yellow, brown, red); if the pigment is black, they are referred to as *melanophores*. The chromatophores, found near the surface of the animal skin, such as those in molluscs, crustacea, and cold-blooded vertebrates, bring color and shade changes to the animal. In many of these animals, the eye is the receptor which through hormonal action initiates the expansion and contraction of the chromatophores.

Invertebrates possess photoreceptors for phototropisms and vision. These have been described and referred to as *eyespots, sensory cells, ocelli,* and *compound eyes.* For vertebrate vison on the other hand, there are completely developed eyes with a lens system for concentrating and focusing the light, and a complex retina with highly differentiated rod and cone cells with their neural connections.

Eyes are not the sole means of photoreception, however, for not only are simple equivalents, "eyespots" involved, but the general body surface may be sensitive to a remarkable degree. We know that the body surface of many eyeless and blinded animals is sensitive to illumination; therefore reference to the "dermal light sense" is used to define this diffuse photosensitivity that can extend over much of the body. There is also some experimental evidence to indicate that deeper tissue cells are photosensitive (Kennedy, 1963); however, the specific receptors responsible for these phenomena are unknown as, for example, certain marine forms which exhibit swimming responses if their spinal cord is exposed to light. There is also the relation of the pineal gland to photosensitivity and control of the pigment effector system in fish. Another light response is known as photoperiodism, which controls such mechanisms as the timing for flowering of plants, pigment migration, sexual cycles, and other such phenomena (Whipple and Hague, 1964). In plants it has been found that photoperiodism can be initiated by light of 6500 Å and inactivated by light further in the red at 7300 Å. All of these phenomena involving light excitation of living systems are areas of much new research. When unravelled, they will contribute to a more complete understanding of how light affects the behavior of living organisms.

There are indications, however, that the process of photoreception depends on a pattern of activity that is fundamentally the same over a wide range of animal forms; therefore, it has been necessary to seek common denominators in the photoreceptive processes that will yield important information on photoresponses of single cells and vision in man.

The photoreceptive processes may be generally formulated as follows:

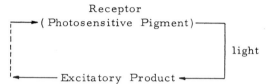

This arrangement is not the only basis for photoreception; rather it is generalized to include stimuli other than light. It may also be the form for all neural excitation; every irritable tissue must contain similar arrangements for reacting with the stimulus, for removing its effect, and for restoring the original system. The peculiar importance of photoreceptor systems rests, therefore, not on their intrinsic form, but on their unique sensitivity to light.

Knowledge of how the vertebrate eye has evolved and how its retinal cells function in transferring the light stimuli from the retina to the cells of the visual cortex of the brain remains generally incomplete.

To find out how light affects the photoreceptor systems of plants and animals, I began to work with a unicellular protozoan algal flagellate, *Euglena*, which, in its ability to photosynthesize, is characteristic of a plant. It has, however, some of the attributes of an animal cell, with eyespots and a flagellum, and its behavior upon light excitation brings about problems similar to those in the origin of nervous excitation.

The approach, then, in attacking this problem, is through a comparative phylogenetic structural and biochemical study of photoreceptors, from the unicellular protozoan eyespots, to multicellular organisms, and finally to the vertebrate retinal rods and cones of man.

In the following chapters, I shall attempt to indicate how these experiments may contribute information and even provide answers to the general problem and often raised question of *how we see*.

Chapter II

EXPERIMENTAL METHODS

To EXPLORE THE phenomena of how photoexcitation is initiated via the retinal cells, it was necessary to determine the molecular architecture and chemistry of a variety of photoreceptors. To do so required the development of more penetrating microanalytical methods and instrumentation to study cell structure and chemistry at the molecular level. Electron microscopy and spectroscopy are two modern methods which have been of tremendous aid in the attempt to gather information on how photoreceptors function in living animals.

ELECTRON MICROSCOPY

Polarizing, phase, and interference microscopy can supply useful information about the structure of cells in their natural state, but their resolution is limited. The electron microscope, however, provides a method to take one to higher orders of magnification < 20 Å $(1\text{Å} = 10^{-4}\mu)$, and hence a resolution which allows us to see molecules with weights less than 50,000. With this increase in magnification and with newer techniques in tissue preparation, resolutions of the order of <5 Å may be obtainable under ideal conditions.

In preparation for electron microscopy, the tissue cells are usually killed and fixed with a metal-containing cellular poison. The processes of cell fixation are extremely complicated, as few metals or cellular poisons are good fixatives. A most useful fixative is 1 per cent osmium tetroxide ($Os\,O_4$), buffered at neutral or alkaline pH (6.8 to 8.5), which increases the electron density and the contrast of the structure. Potassium permanganate, which has also been used as a fixative, has revealed *fine structure* not observed with osmium tetroxide. Other fixatives such as potassium chromate and dichromate, platinum chloride, uranyl nitrate, lead and vanadium salts and combinations of these have been used to enhance structural detail. Histochemical methods have also been applied.

[7]

The fixed material is embedded after dehydration in acrylics (e.g., n-butyl methacrylate), epoxides, or other resins, which when polymerized possess the right hardness and ductility for thin-sectioning. Sections $<0.05\mu$ in thickness are cut from the polymerized block on a special microtome (e.g., Porter-Blum) with a glass or a diamond knife. Sections of this thickness permit electron penetration, so that rather than viewing a shadow or a replica of the tissue section, we are able to see through it as in the light microscope.

In attempts to overcome the inadequacies of these methods, techniques in freeze-drying, such as rapid freezing with Helium II are being investigated (Fernández-Morán, 1960, 1961). Negative staining is another method for viewing the specimen. Here the sample section is suspended in distilled H_2O, placed on electron microscope grids and allowed to air dry. The grids are then floated, specimen side down on 5 per cent uranyl acetate for three hours, rinsed with distilled H_2O, and placed in 1 per cent phosphotungstic acid (PTA) for ten seconds. The excess PTA is removed, the sample dried and then examined in the electron microscope. These methods are described and summarized in several recent texts on electron microscopy (Siegel, 1964; Pease, 1960; Kay, 1963).

SPECTROSCOPY

Pigments are characterized by their absorption spectra. The systematic investigation of absorption spectra has been of great value in establishing the identity and structure of numerous compounds.

The theory which makes absorption measurements meaningful is derived from Lambert's and Beer's Laws.

Lambert's Law is known as

$$I_x = I_o e^{-\mu x}$$

I_o is the intensity of the entering light, I_x is the intensity of the transmitted light through the sample, and μ is the absorption coefficient. This is the correct form of Lambert's Law only if μ is constant over the wavelength. In this case, the initial intensity I_o is represented as an integral over the range of wavelengths present.

$$I_o = \int I_{o\lambda} d\lambda$$

where $I_o \lambda d\lambda$ is the incident intensity between $\lambda + d\lambda$. For each

$I_o d\lambda$, μ will be constant, so a more general form of Lambert's Law is

$$I = \int I_{o\lambda} e^{-\mu x} d\lambda$$

These integral equations are complicated and difficult to use in this form.

Since absorption is a probability phenomenon, one expects that the more absorbers there are in the path of the light the greater will be the absorption.

For solutions with low concentrations, when Lambert's Law is valid,

$$\mu = \beta c$$

where c is the concentration of the absorbing molecule, and β the extinction coefficient is referred to as "Beer's Law."

Provided that Beer's Law is valid, it is possible to determine the contribution to μ, the absorption coefficient, of any one type of compound by measuring μ for solutions with and without the compound. The difference of the two values of μ rather than the two absolute values is important. Most spectrophotometers are constructed to read the difference directly.

In actual practice, instead of μ, which is defined by

$$\mu = \frac{1}{x} \ln \frac{I_o}{I}$$

the optical density D is measured, where

$$D = \log_{10} \frac{I_o}{I}$$

The two are simply related, since

$$\log_{10}\left(\frac{I_o}{I}\right) = \frac{1}{2.3}\left[\ln \frac{I_o}{I}\right]$$

one may write

$$\mu = \frac{D}{2.3\,x}$$

The values of μ and β may be specified in a number of ways, depending on the units for x and c, usually x $=$ 1 cm. Different symbols are often used for the same form. The most widely used coefficient is ϵmM.

In Table I, some of the more common terms used in the literature are given. With these units, one may use measured optical densities to compute concentrations and to identify molecular species. Familiarity with the symbols and units listed allows one to compare and correlate absorption characteristics reported by different authors.

TABLE I

Symbols Used in Absorption Spectrophotometry

Term	Symbol	Alternative equation	Defining equation	Units
1. Transmittance	τ	T	$\tau = 100 \, (I/I_o)$	Per cent
2. Optical density	D	O.D., E,D	$D = \log_{10} (I/Io)$	Pure number
3. Extinction coefficient	ε	K	$\varepsilon = D/x$	x in cm. ε in cm.$^{-1}$
4. Specific extinction coefficient	ε_{sp}	ε	$\varepsilon_{sp} = \dfrac{D}{cx}$	c in gm/L ε_{sp} in L/(gm. cm.)
5. Molar extinction coefficient	ε_{mol}	$\varepsilon_M, \varepsilon$ E	$\varepsilon_{mol} = \dfrac{D}{cx}$	c in moles/L ε_{mol} in L/mole cm.
6. Millimolar extinction coefficient	ε_{mM}	ε	$\varepsilon_{mM} = \dfrac{D}{cx}$	c in millimoles/L
			$\varepsilon_{mM} = \dfrac{\varepsilon_{mole}}{1,000}$	ε_{mM} in L/(millimole cm.)
7. Absorption coefficient	μ	k, a	$\mu = \dfrac{1}{x} \ln(I/Io)$	μ in cm^{-1}
8. Molar absorption coefficient (extinction coefficient)	β	βmol	$\beta = \dfrac{\mu}{c}$	L/(mole. cm.)

Taken in part from Ackerman (1962). Absorbance is also used for O.D.

MICROSPECTROPHOTOMETRY

A spectroscopic method that can be applied to the quantitative study of the chemistry of single cells and their organelles (e.g., nucleus, chloroplasts, retinal rods and cones), is microspectrophotometry. This was recognized in the late 1930's by Caspersson, in Sweden, who initiated the development of microspectrophotometric instrumentation for ultraviolet absorption spectroscopy and techniques for the study of the chemistry of the nucleic acids of the cell nucleus (Caspersson, 1950, 1961; Caspersson and Lomakka, 1962; Caspersson *et al.*, 1955). The instrumentation for microspectrophotometry and its application to the chemistry of biological tissue cells is being continuously developed (Swift and Rasch, 1956; Wallace, 1958; Pollister and Ornstein, 1959; Mongomery, 1962; Liebman, 1962; MacNichol, 1964; Brown, 1961; Wolken and Strother, 1963).

The microspectrophotometers presently in use are laboratory-built instruments. The essential elements of all these microspectrophotometers are a monochromatic light source, a microscope, a light chopper, a sensitive photocell (usually a photomultiplier tube), an amplifier, and an output device, usually a recorder. With reflecting and quartz optics, a spectral range from the ultraviolet through the visible can be obtained. Living, fixed, and stained tissue cells have been studied by measuring the absorption spectrum of specimen areas as small as 0.5μ. Information on cellular constituents can be obtained by scanning specimen areas at fixed wavelengths when their specific absorption peaks are known, for example, nucleic acids, porphyrins, cytochromes.

Most instruments, with the exception of the simplified microspectrophotometers (Denton, 1959; Strother and Wolken, 1959), are elaborate ones, employing either split or dual-beam optical systems with mechanical beam chopping devices, voltage-regulated photomultiplier tubes with feedback mechanisms, and automatic recording outputs (Caspersson, 1961; Chance, *et al.*, 1959). Quantitative measurements of the optical density of a given specimen with an instrumental error of less than 5 per cent can be obtained. The response times of the instruments may be of the order of milliseconds, and measurements from the ultraviolet through the visible are recorded in a few minutes.

A simplified microspectrophotometer (M-1) was designed and constructed in our laboratory (Strother and Wolken, 1959). Figure 1 includes a diagram of the basic design of the instrument, indicating that the light from source L (Xenon arc or tungsten ribbon filament), enters a grating monochromator, G, and that the exit slit of the monochromator is focused by a quartz lens on the condenser of the microscope, M. The microscope is equipped with reflecting objectives (50 X with numerical aperture of 0.5, American Optical Company). The light passes through the specimen to the CdSe photoconductive cell, C, the light-sensitive element, which is accurately positioned relative to the image (25 cm. above the eyepiece of the microscope).

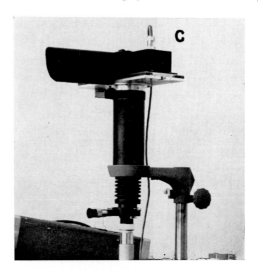

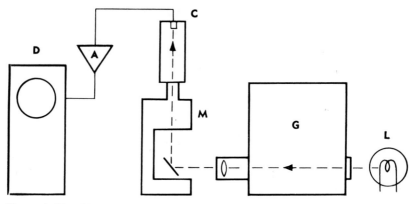

Figure 1 Simplified microspectrophotometer (M-1) and diagram indicating L, light source; G, monochromator; M, microscope with reflecting optics; C, photoconductive cell; A, dc amplifier; D, oscilloscope (in place of A and D, a dc voltmeter can also be used). The photograph shows housing for photocell and viewer mounted on sliding track.

The electrical signal from the photocell is either amplified by the dc amplifier A and displayed on an oscilloscope D or read from a high-impedance dc voltmeter. With these components, the instrument is usable over the wavelength range from 200 to 900 mμ in a single sweep. (Using a tungsten ribbon light source, the useful range is from 370 to 900 mμ.)

Photoconductive CdSe cells have been used for spectral measurements in the infrared region and for x-ray spectroscopy (Henry and Cole, 1959). The photoconductive cells being used at present are special purpose cells (manufactured by the Clairex Corporation of New York) with a photosensitive surface of 0.5 by 1 mm. and a radiation sensitivity per unit area roughly equivalent to a photomultiplier tube. They do not require high voltages. The spectral response of the cadmium selenide cells extends from the far ultraviolet to the near infrared at about 1μ. The peak response is in the visible region at 720 mμ. At high light intensity, the time constant of the cell is of the order of milliseconds. At extremely low light levels, the time constant is of the order of seconds.

The maximum magnification employed is 500 X. No limiting apertures are used in this instrument, since the entire photosensitive surface is used for measurements. The noise level, as determined by photocell current fluctuations, is about 2 x 10^{-3} optical density units. Since the entire photosurface of the cell is exposed to the light beam, no effects due to variation in the sensitivity of the photosurface are observed.

The procedure for obtaining an absorption spectrum with the apparatus is relatively simple. The area of interest in the specimen is located on a marked ground glass screen at the top of the apparatus. The photocell is then put into position, and the dark current is balanced out with a separate bias voltage. At each desired wavelength setting, one reading is taken over the specimen and another over a reference area.

Recorded data and faster time responses than those available with the simplified microspectrophotometer are needed for the spectroscopy of photosensitive pigments. As a result, a modification of our simplified microspectrophotometer, a single-beam recording microspectrophotometer, using either a photoconductive cell or a photomultiplier, was developed (Wolken and Strother, 1963). A photograph of the automated instrument (M-3) is shown in Figure 2a, and a schematic diagram of its design in Figure 2b.

For kinetic studies, a temperature-controlled specimen chamber with thermoelectric elements has been constructed and adapted to the microscope stage; temperatures from —20° to + 100°C. are

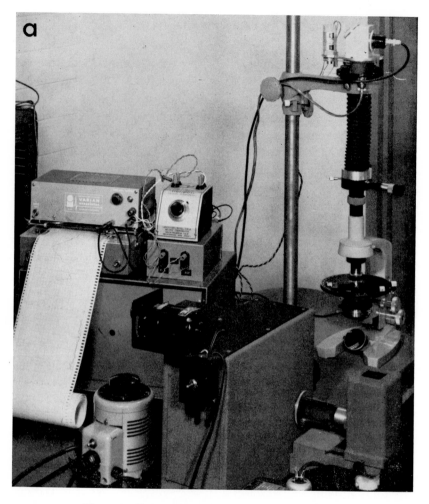

Figure 2a Recording microspectrophotometer M-3.

easily obtained in the specimen chamber, and much lower temperatures are possible (Fig. 3a). Living cells can be grown in this tissue cell chamber and scanned at periodic intervals to study the biosynthesis of pigments. The effects of temperature and wavelength on the synthesis and bleaching of pigments in the photoreceptors can also be followed. The infrared image converter (Fig. 3b) permits us to locate the retinal rods and cones without bleaching their photosensitive pigments. The instrument is ideally suited for scanning

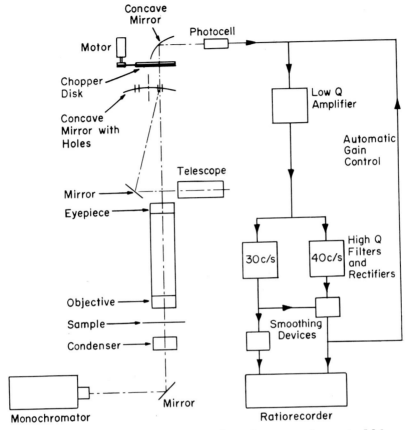

Figure 2b Schematic diagram of recording microspectrophotometer M-3.

single living cells at fixed wavelengths and for locating those cell constituents with characteristic absorption peaks. It can also be used for spectral analysis of fixed and stained cells. High resolving power can be achieved at low magnification, and data from the ultraviolet, visible, and near infrared regions of the spectrum can be easily obtained. Examples of recorded absorption spectrums for a chloroplast and a frog red blood cell are shown in Figures 4 and 5. Other spectra are illustrated in the text.

Analytical methods such as ultracentrifugation, chromatography, tissue culture, and the use of microelectrodes in electrophysiology are described in the experiments in which they have been used to explore the receptor-cell chemistry and physiology.

Figure 3a Temperature control stage, using thermoelectric device for microscope.
Figure 3b Infrared image converter attached to microscope for specimen location
to prevent bleaching of photosensitive pigments.

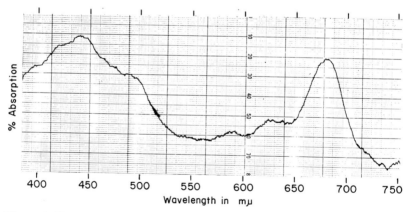

Figure 4 Absorption spectrum of *Euglena* chloroplast, using M-3 recording instrument; peak positions and heights compare to chlorophyll *a*.

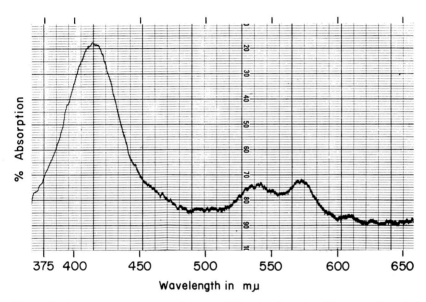

Figure 5 Absorption spectrum of frog red blood cell, using M-3 recording instrument.

Chapter III

THE VERTEBRATE EYE

THE STRUCTURE OF THE EYE AND IMAGING

THE OPTICS OF image formation was described in 1611 by Johannes Kepler, and by Rene Descartes in 1664. At the end of the seventeenth century, William Molyneux 1709 of Dublin wrote the first treatise on optics in English, which contained several simple diagrams comparing the projection of a real, inverted image with that of the human eye.

What types of imaging eyes are there? In the invertebrates there are two kinds of optical systems for imaging, one of which is referred to as the "pin-hole" eye because it employes the principle of the pin-hole camera; an opaque chamber pierced by a small hole that allows the passage of only a very narrow pencil of light from each point in the external scene. By this means, an inverted image is formed on the opposite wall of the chamber (Fig. 6a). This kind of image-forming device is not very efficient, for only a small fraction of the light emitted by an object can get to the photoreceptor surface. If the hole is made larger to increase the amount of light, image definition is lost. If it is made smaller to improve the definition, it is defeated by diffraction effects. This type of eye has the advantage of simplicity because no focusing is required for near or for distant objects. The size of the image is inversely proportional to the distance of the object.

The other is the compound eye, which forms an image through a bundle of tubes that contain the photoreceptor surfaces and which are separated by opaque walls. Only light falling on a particular tube in the direction of its axis can proceed to the end of the tube and reach the photoreceptors to form an erect image of the object (Fig. 6b). The image formed is the same size as the object, regardless of distance. Therefore, only those objects equal to or smaller than the device can be imaged completely, and no impression of

[18]

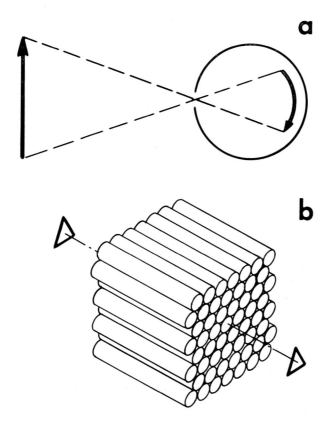

Figure 6a Pin hole imaging system.
Figure 6b Compound imaging system.

distance by perspective can be conveyed since the image size remains unchanged with object distance. However, if the tubes are disposed around the surface of a sphere or segments of a sphere with their axes pointing to the center, these disadvantages are avoided.

Another kind of optical system is found for most vertebrate eyes, in which the image is formed by the refraction of light on one or more spherical surfaces that separate media of different refractive indexes. This causes the formation of inverted, reduced images on the retinal surface. The refracting eye has the great advantage in that image formation occurs through an integrative action, so that all rays falling on the eye from a given point are brought to a point of focus on the photoreceptors (the retinal rods and cones). The image is inverted, and its size is inversely proportional to the distance of the object. The combined optical and sensory apparatus is paired in two symmetrically constructed and oriented eyeballs. As a result, a large section of visual space is imaged on both retinas

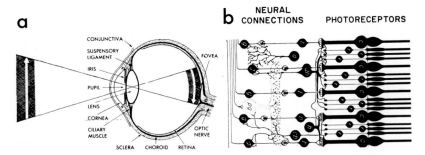

Figure 7a Schematic of human vertebrate eye.

Figure 7b Schematic retina showing photoreceptors and neural connections.

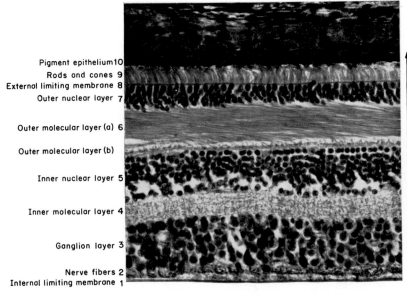

Figure 8 Section of human retina, showing its 10 cell layers. X 165

binocularly. Types of refracting eyes are also found in some invertebrates, e.g., the molluscs, *Octopus and Squid.*

The development of the vertebrate eye consists principally in the conversion of the cells of the optic cup walls into the retina. This involves the multiplication of cells and the conversion of some of them into the light-sensitive rods and cones, and others into the nerve cells with which the rods and cones are connected and which in turn connect with the brain. Although the original connection of the optic vesicle with the embryonic brain persists throughout this process (as the optic stalk), nervous connection of the retina with the brain is secondary and is formed by outgrowth of nerve fibers from the nerve cells of the retina through the optic stalk into the brain.

The gross anatomy of a section of the human eye and its parts is shown schematically in the diagram Figure 7a and b. The eyeball, which is approximately spherical, houses the complete optical apparatus; two refracting structures, the clear *cornea* and the crystalline *lens* (note its structure in Fig. 9). A variable aperture, a diaphragm, is provided by a contractile, membranous partition, the *iris*, that regulates the size of the light opening, the *pupil*. There are excellent descriptions of the eye and its histology in many textbooks of ophthalmology (Walls, 1942; Polyak, 1957; Duke-Elder, 1958, and Last, 1961).

Since our main interest is with the sensory cells of the retina and their connection with the nervous cell layers, it is best to begin with the anatomy of the retina.

The vertebrate retina is a complex structure which is closely attached to the pigment epithelium. It consists of nine layers (shown in Fig. 8): the photoreceptors, the rods and cones that are arranged in a single-layered mosaic (Fig. 10a, b and c) with a highly developed system of connecting and inter-connecting neurons; the external limiting membrane; the external nuclear layer; the external molecular (plexiform) layer; the internal nuclear layer; the internal (plexiform) layer; the ganglion cell layer; the nerve fiber layer; and the internal limiting membrane. The nervous layers comprise the rod and cone cells, the bipolar cells, and the ganglion cells. It is

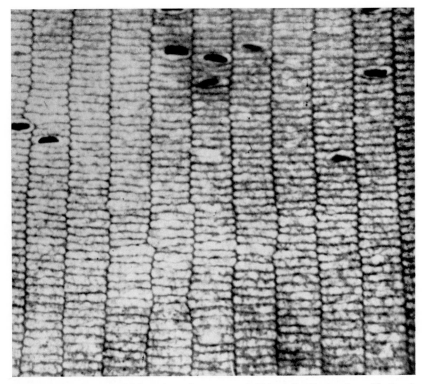

Figure 9 Section of chicken lens (courtesy of Dr. A.J. Coulombre, National Institutes of Health, Bethesda, Maryland).

estimated that in the human retina, there are 1×10^8 retinal rods and 7×10^6 retinal cones, and in the foveal area, 4×10^3 retinal cones.

Next to the retina is a sheet of cells filled with black pigment, the *choroid coat,* that absorbs extra light and prevents internally reflected light from blurring the image.

The first four layers constitute the neuro-epithelial layer and are the neurons of the first order. The remaining layers are considered the cerebral portion where there exists a complex arrangement of nervous elements resembling, in structure and function, those of the central nervous system of which the retina represents an outlying portion. The fifth layer (internal nuclear layer), which contains the bipolar, horizontal, and amacrine cells, and the sixth layer, comprise the neurons of the second order. The seventh and eighth

layers make up the neurons of the third order, which pass cen-
tripetally to the primary optic center (the lateral geniculate) of the
metathalmus (refer to description in Polyak, 1957).

Figure 10 Human retina.
    a. Folded section of the retina photoreceptors.
    b. Cross-section.

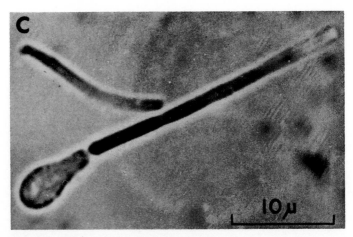

Figure 10c Isolated single human retina rod.

Chapter IV

PHOTORECEPTOR PIGMENTS

CAROTENOIDS

PHOTOSENSITIVITY depends upon the absorption of light and upon a pigment or pigment system capable of absorbing that light.

All plants and animals that exhibit phototropisms, phototaxis, and vision, have been shown to depend upon carotenoid molecules or their derivatives for photoreceptor function. The evidence for this is that the action spectrum (spectral response of their behavior) resembles the absorption spectrum of carotenoids.

The cartotenoids are yellow, orange, or red, fat-soluble pigments that are widely distributed in plant and animal cells. Generically, they are named for their most familiar substance, carotene, and are divided into two main groups: *carotenes* (hydrocarbons) the most abundant of which is the all-trans β-carotene $C_{40}H_{56}$ (Figs. 12 and 15), and the *xanthophylls* (oxygen-containing derivatives). One of the common xanthophylls is lutein $C_{40}H_{54}(OH)_2$, or luteol. The oxygen atoms can be in hydroxyl, epoxide, carboxyl, or methoxyl groups. From the structure elucidated by Karrer (in Karrer and Jucker, 1950), carotenoids can be considered as being built up from isoprene units. The linear portion of the molecule consists of four radicals of isoprene (2-methyl-1, 3-butadiene) residues. The isoprene units are linked so that the two methyl groups nearest the center of the molecule are in positions 1:6, while all other lateral methyl groups are in position 1:5. The structure of the carotenoids is illustrated in Figure 11.

The carotenoid molecule, then, is made up of a chromophoric system of alternate single and double interatomic linkages, so-called conjugated double bonds between the carbon atoms of a long chain. The carotenoids possess 40 carbon atoms in the molecule.

The large number of these conjugated double bonds offers the possibility of either *cis* or *trans* geometric configurations. Zechmeister

[25]

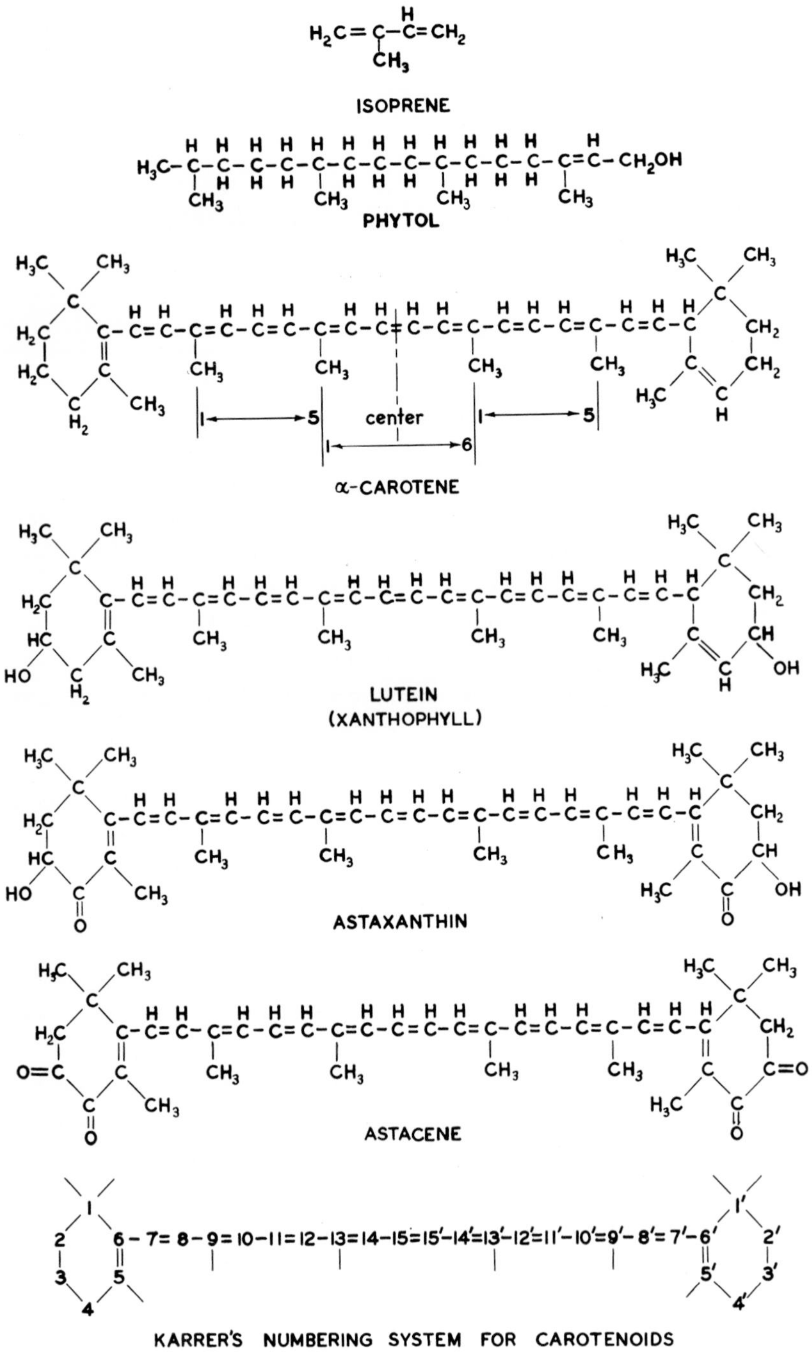

Figure 11 Molecular structure of carotenoids (Karrer's numbering system).

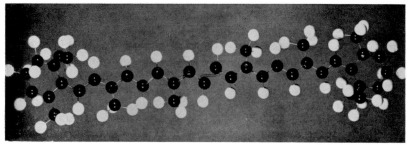

β Carotene (all trans)

Figure 12 Structural model of β-carotene.

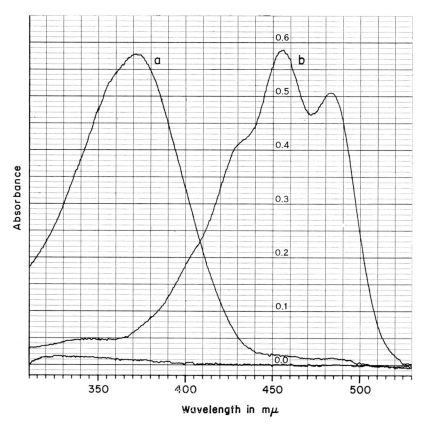

Figure 13 Absorption spectra.
    a. Retinene₁ in benzene.
    b. β-carotene in benzene.

(1944) calculated that there are possibly 20 geometric isomers of β-carotene, of which 6 *cis* isomers have been discovered in nature. The spectral characteristics, and therefore the color of the carotenoids, are largely determined by the number of conjugated double bonds in their molecules. (Fig. 13b shows the absorption spectrum of all-*trans* β-carotene in benzene).

Less is known of the manner of biosynthesis of carotenoids, but it is known that they are genetically associated with the 20-carbon atom, aliphatic alcohol phytol, which is the colorless moiety of the ester-comprising chlorophyll (Figs. 11 and 14). The striking resemblance between the carotenoid skeleton and phytol also holds for the details of spacial configuration (Fig. 11). Studies of the action spectra for chlorophyll and carotenoid synthesis (in *Euglena*) indicate that a similar precursor, probably a porphyrin molecule, influences both chlorophyll and carotenoid synthesis (Wolken and Mellon, 1956).

This brief description of the carotenoid pigments is helpful only as an introduction to our discussion of the visual pigments of the retinal cells. A more comprehensive discussion of the biosynthesis and chemical structure of the carotenoids and their distribution throughout the plant and animal kingdom is found in (Strain, 1944, 1951; Zechmeister, 1944, 1962; Karrer and Jucker, 1950; Goodwin, 1952; and Fox, 1953).

Other pigments, such as the melanins, the haems (e.g., haemoglobin, cytochromes), and the flavins, are also found in the eye. The carotenoids, however, play the central role in the biochemical evolution from the C_{40} polyenes to the C_{20} polyenes (β-carotene$\rightarrow$vitamin A), from plant and animal phototropisms to vision in man.

Carotenoids are easily and abundantly synthesized by plants. The important change that has occurred in animals is that they can no longer synthesize the carotenoids and must obtain them in their nutrition from plants. Therefore, it is not the ingested plant carotenoids but the degraded derivative, vitamin A, that is necessary for vision (Fig. 15). The general function of vitamin A is to support growth and to maintain the tissue cells. Signs of vitamin A deficiency (in the rat) are loss of weight, postural imbalance, respiratory disturbances, corneal opacities, disarrangement of coat,

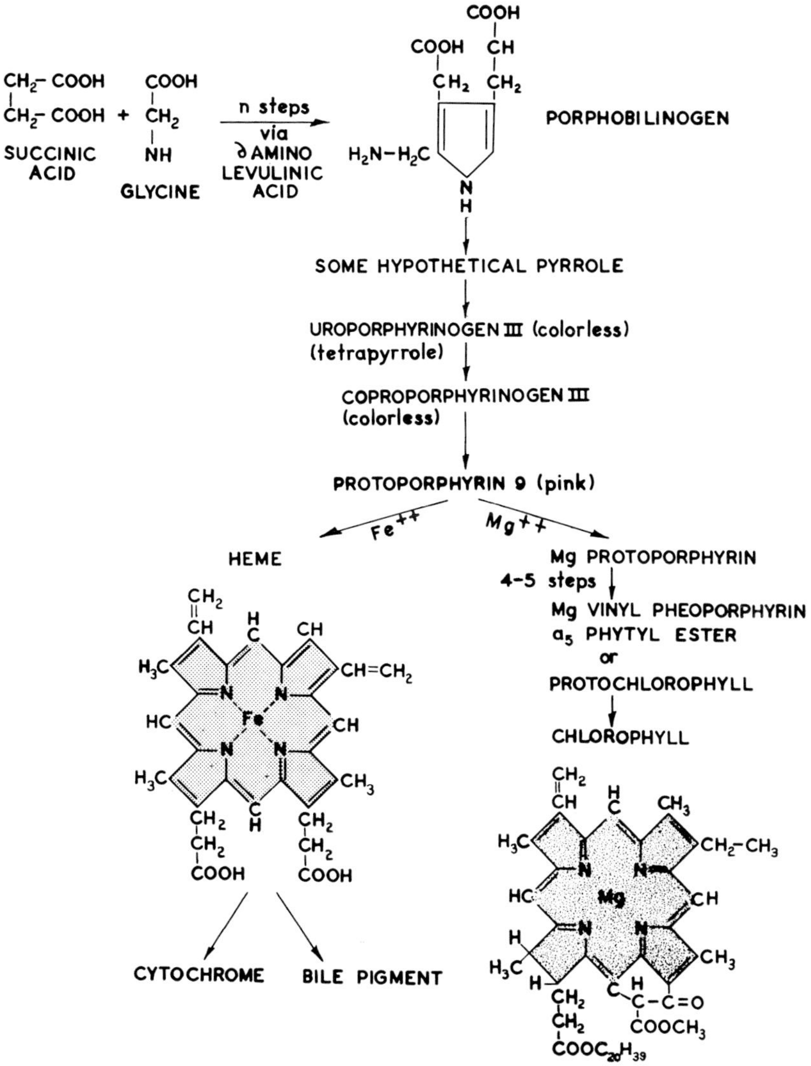

Figure 14 Granick's scheme for the biosynthesis of porphyrins.

and red secretions about the eye. Tissues, particularly the epithelia, begin to disintegrate, and within days the animal dies (Moore, 1957).

To appreciate this function of vitamin A in animals, it is best to turn directly to its role in the eye and vision.

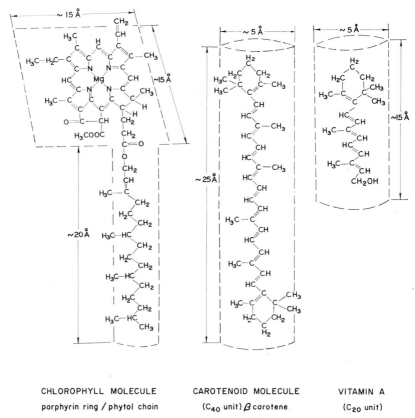

CHLOROPHYLL MOLECULE   CAROTENOID MOLECULE   VITAMIN A

porphyrin ring / phytol chain   (C_{40} unit) β carotene   (C_{20} unit)

Figure 15 Comparative structure of chlorophyll, β-carotene, and vitamin A molecules. Note relationship in structure of phytol C_{20} of the chlorophyll molecule to β-carotene and to vitamin A—structures.

VITAMIN A AND VISION

After the initial stores of vitamin A in the liver and blood have been exhausted, the first symptom of vitamin A deficiency in man and in other animals is the rise of visual threshold known as night blindness. This is the only symptom of which the cause is understood.

To learn something of the tissue function of vitamin A* ($C_{19}H_{27}$ CH_2OH), vitamin A acid ($C_{19}H_{27}COOH$) was employed. Vitamin A acid was first prepared by Arens and van Dorp (1946) and

---

*New nomenclature for vitamin A is *retinol;* vitamin A aldehyde (retinene) is *retinal;* vitamin A acid is *retonic acid.*

van Dorp and Arens (1946), and was shown to maintain growth in the rat and to stave off obvious signs of deficiency with a biopotency approaching that of vitamin A itself. Yet no matter how large the amounts in which the acid was fed, no vitamin A was deposited in the liver. The rat was unable to reduce vitamin A acid to vitamin A or to the alcohol, the form in which vitamin A is stored. This special circumstance led Moore (1953) to suggest that although the tissue functions of vitamin A seem to be fulfilled by vitamin A acid, this substance might not be able to serve as the precursor of the visual pigments, which need for their synthesis the vitamin A and vitamin A aldehyde. For this reason, rats maintained on vitamin A acid, although growing normally and in otherwise good condition, became extremely night blind and eventually blind. According to Dowling and Wald (1960), the general metabolism of vitamin A in the rat seems to involve the relationship found in Table II.

The importance of vitamin A aldehyde as an intermediate in vitamin A metabolism was emphasized when it was demonstrated that $retinene_1$ is vitamin A_1 aldehyde (while $retinene_2$ is vitamin A_2 aldehyde). Morton (1944) and Morton and Goodwin (1944) first suggested and confirmed that $retinene_1$ must be the vitamin A aldehyde. Then Glover, Goodwin, and Morton (1948) demonstrated that $retinene_1$ is rapidly converted to vitamin A_1 when it is administered orally, subcutaneously, or intraperitoneally. The conversion of vitamin A aldehyde to vitamin A alcohol is a reduction which occurs in the gut and in subcutaneous tissues. This was also a plausible explanation for the displacement of the absorption maximum (de-

TABLE II

GENERAL METABOLISM OF VITAMIN A

Vitamin A ⇌ Vitamin A Aldehyde ⟶ Vitamin A Acid
(transport)   (growth and tissue
                                                Maintenance)

      | light   opsin   ?

Vitamin A   Visual Pigments   Inactive Products
Esters
(tissue storage)

From: Dowling and Wald (1960).

pending on the organic solvent) from around 328 mμ, that of vitamin A, to about 370 mμ, that of retinene$_1$ (Fig. 13a). The change in the absorption spectrum can then be explained by an increase in the number of conjugated bonds from 5 to 6; if the terminal ___CH$_2$OH group of vitamin A is replaced by a ___CHO the aldehyde group, this would provide the sixth conjungated bond (Fig. 18).

Vitamin A aldehyde has been prepared by a number of workers. Morton and Goodwin (1944) were able to prepare the aldehyde by shaking vitamin A concentrates dissolved in light petroleum either with dilute aqueous potassium permanganate containing sulfuric acid. On chromatographic separation, a fraction had an absorption maximum at 365-370 mμ in saturated hydrocarbon solvents, and 385 mμ in chloroform. When reacted with antimony trichloride, the maximum peak was at 665 mμ. Hawkins and Hunter (1944) likewise synthesized vitamin A$_1$ aldehyde from vitamin A$_1$, and Hunter and Williams (1945) obtained the aldehyde by the oxidation of β-carotene. This is of great interest, as it provides chemical proof for the conversion of β-carotene to vitamin A. Retinene$_1$ may also be an intermediate product in the transformation of β-carotene to vitamin A$_1$ *in vivo*.

Van Dorp and Arens (1947) synthesized the vitamin A$_1$ aldehyde in the course of a synthesis of vitamin A alcohol. A procedure for the preparation of vitamin A$_1$ aldehyde has been given by Ball, Goodwin and Morton (1948) in which vitamin A$_1$ was oxidized in light petroleum with manganese dioxide for six to ten days in the dark with high yields (80%) of the aldehyde being obtained. The vitamin A$_1$ aldehyde was then fractionated chromatographically on an alumina column and further purified by crystallization from petroleum ether at —72°C. After recrystallization, reddish-brown crystals were obtained which melted at 56.5 to 58°C., and which showed a single maximum absorption peak in cyclohexane at 373 mμ. A final recrystallization from petroleum ether left large clusters of predominantly needle-like, orange-red crystals that melted at 61-62°C. The crystalline vitamin A$_1$ aldehyde reacted with antimony trichloride to give an absorption spectrum maximum at 664 mμ.

Morton et al. (1946, 1947) based on the conversion of retinene$_2$

to vitamin A_2 when fed to rats, demonstrated that vitamin A_2 aldehyde is the same as retinene$_2$.

Wald (1938, 1939) was the first to prepare retinene$_2$ from the frog retina. He characterized it as a deep yellow substance soluble in petroleum ether. It was first obtained in crystalline form by Salah and Morton (1948). The absorption maxima of crystalline retinene$_2$ were found to be 385 mμ in cyclohexane, 388 mμ in light petroleum ether, 395 mμ in ethanol, and 406 mμ in chloroform. Retinene$_2$ also reacts with antimony trichloride, showing an absorption maximum at 703 mμ.

The Visual Pigment, Rhodopsin

As one goes from dim to bright light, from rod to cone vision, the sensitivity of the eye shifts toward the red end of the spectrum. This phenomenon was first described in 1825 by the Czech physiologist, Johannes Purkinje. He noticed that with the first light of dawn, blue objects tend to look bright compared with red, but that they begin to look dimmer as the morning advances. The basis of this change is because of a large difference in spectral sensitivity between rods and cones.

The visual responses can be studied in terms of reaction to light, controlling the intensity and the wavelength of light and observing the behavior of the animal. Man is an excellent experimental subject in this case, for we can ask him what he sees and interpret his reply in terms of the physics of the light stimulus. This area of visual research, known as the psychophysics of vision, has given us considerable data on visual thresholds and color discrimination.

Rods have their maximal sensitivity in the blue-green at about 500 mμ; the entire spectral sensitivity of the cones is transposed toward the red, lying in the yellow-green at about 562 mμ (see absorption spectrum for iodopsin, Fig. 17). There are shifts in these absorption maxima depending on the animal species and their environment.

The photosensitive pigments upon which the visual threshold depends are either retinene$_1$ or retinene$_2$ (retinal), vitamin A_1 or A_2 aldehydes complexed with the protein, opsin. The extracted visual pigment-complexes are identified by their absorption spectra as *rho-*

dopsin (retinene₁ + rod opsin), or *porphyropsin* (retinene₂ + rod opsin) in the rods; and *iodopsin* (retinene₁ + cone opsin) or *cyanopsin* (retinene₂ + cone opsin) for the retinal cones (Fig. 16 and their absorption spectrums in Fig. 17).

The mechanism of the visual process in the vertebrate retinal rod has been studied vigorously by Wald (1953-56, 1959-61a) and Dartnall (1957, 1962). The visual pigment, rhodopsin, bleaches upon exposure to light and yields retinene and opsin. The retinene is then reduced to vitamin A by the action of the enzymes, alcohol

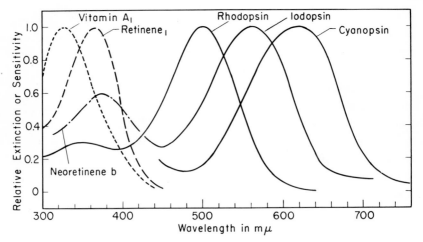

Figure 16. The visual pigments in the rods and cones, derived from vitamin A₁ and retinene₁, Vitamin A₂ and retinene₂; and their absorption peaks. (Wald, 1959).

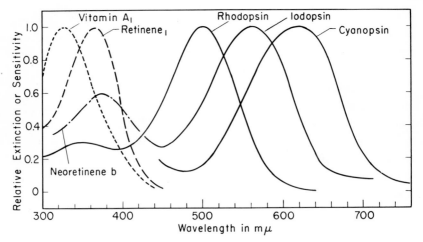

Figure 17 Absorption spectra of the visual pigments. (from Wald, 1959)

dehydrogenase and diphosphopyridine nucleotide in the reduced state (DPNH). However, the direction of the equilibrium is to favor the production of vitamin A, so that almost all of the retinene formed is quickly reduced to vitamin A. Rhodopsin is regenerated in the dark by a reversal of this procedure; retinene combines with opsin to form rhodopsin (see Fig. 16). The reaction is spontaneous, and opsin may, therefore, be looked upon as a retinene-trapping agent, removing free retinene from the mixture and causing the production of additional retinene from vitamin A to maintain the equilibrium.

Vitamin A and retinene are polyene chains that can exist in a number of different geometrical configurations corresponding to the possible cis-trans isomerization around the different double bonds of these molecules (indicated in Fig. 18 and Table III). The retinene which combines with opsin to form rhodopsin is not identical with the retinene formed upon bleaching. Because of the system of conjugated double bonds and asymmetric carbon atoms present in the retinene molecule, it can exist in a variety of isomeric forms (Table III).

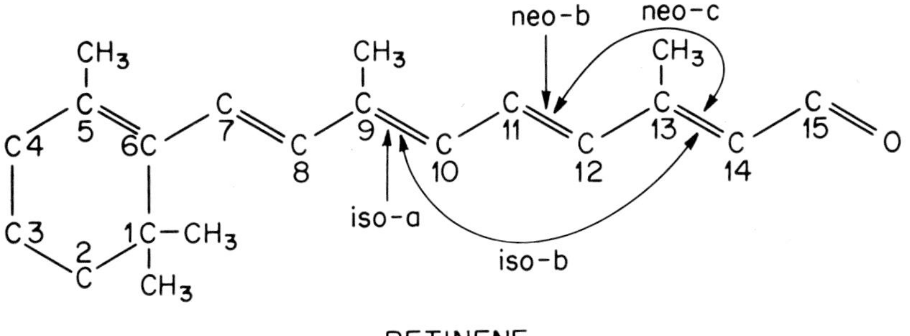

RETINENE

Figure 18 Molecular structure of retinene₁ showing possible different geometric isomers.

TABLE III

Isomerization around bonds	Nomenclature	Name
9-10	9-*cis*	iso-*a*
11-12	11-*cis*	neo-*b*
13-14	13-*cis*	neo-*a*
9-10, 13-14	9, 13-di-*cis*	iso-*b*
11-12, 13-14	11, 13-di-*cis*	neo-*c*

These are five in number: an all-trans and isomeric forms representing rotation about the 9-10 carbon bond; the 11-12 bond; the 13-14 bond; and both the 9-10 and 13-14 bonds. The numbering of the carbon atoms corresponds to Karrer's scheme for the numbering of carbon atoms in the carotenoid molecule. The retinene produced by the bleaching of the rhodopsin has been found to be always of the all-trans form. To resynthesize rhodopsin from all-trans retinene, retinene must be isomerized to the 11-cis (neo-b) form (representing rotation around the 11-12 bond) to recombine with opsin. This isomerization takes place in the light and involves all five forms.

The existance of the 11-cis isomer was considered improbable, because the steric interference of the methyl group fixed at carbon 13, with the hydrogen at position 10 would prevent the molecules from being entirely planar. Professor Wald and his associates were surprised when they found that the very isomer of retinene which is in the vertebrate visual complex is the 11-cis configuration of retinene. This isomer is the most easily formed upon irradiation, and the most sensitive to temperature and light. Because of its hindered configuration, the 11-cis form is the least stable of the isomers, and Wald feels that this, rather than the presence of a more stable form, explains its presence in the rhodopsin molecule.

The bleaching of rhodopsin to form retinene and opsin does not proceed directly, but in a series of steps. The important step is the isomerization of neo-b retinene to all-trans retinene, resulting in release of energy (due to the transformation to a more stable form). This single step results in the conversion of rhodopsin to lumirhodopsin. It is followed immediately by a thermal rearrangement of the opsin molecule which produces metarhodopsin. At low temperatures, lumirhodopsin is stable. At temperatures of —65°C., Hubbard, Brown, and Kropf (1959) found that no metarhodopsin is formed upon illumination of rhodopsin or lumirhodopsin, and that no rhodopsin can be synthesized from metarhodopsin. A thermal rearrangement of the opsin molecule is therefore believed to be involved in the transition between lumirhodopsin and metarhodopsin. Finally, the removal of the all-trans retinene from the metarhodopsin yields free retinene and opsin. This final step, it is believed, may also proceed by way of an intermediate; first a further (and much slower) rearrangement of the opsin molecule, proceeding to still another retinene-protein complex, designated as indicator yellow, and second, the removal of the retinene.

Light-induced changes of rhodopsin are not normally reversible, but at temperatures between —196° and —140°C., the pigment is reversibly photochromic (Yoshizawa and Wald, 1963): rhodopsin (λ max = 498 mμ) $\rightleftarrows$ pre-lumirhodopsin (λ max = 540 mμ). Light of 440 mμ favors the forward reaction, while light of 600 mμ drives the reaction to the left. These changes apparently involve the isomerization of 11-cis retinene to the all-trans form with little change of the protein. As the temperature is raised, pre-lumirhodopsin goes over to lumirhodopsin, presumably as the protein, opsin opens. In the transformation of rhodopsin to metarhodopsin, two additional SH groups become exposed, and one H^+ binding group per molecule. By this time, excitation has occurred. Metarhodopsin then slowly hydrolysizes, except in some invertebrate retinas to a mixture of all-trans retinene and opsin. Wald *et al.* (1963) have suggested that rhodopsin may be a pro-enzyme which is transformed by light to the active enzyme, metarhodopsin.

Purification of Rhodopsin

Methods for extracting rhodopsin involve the separation of the retinal rods from the retinal tissue. The retinas are dissected in dim red light, shaken in physiological saline 0.9 NaCl or in 1.32 M sucrose. The isolated rod outer segments are then centrifuged in a sucrose gradient, which throws the fibrous material, blood cells, and melanin granules to the bottom of the tube, while the retinal rods remain suspended in the supernatant. The rods are then hardened in 4 per cent alum solution, extracted in 1-2 per cent digitonin, centrifuged, and buffered to various pHs. There are many variations on these procedures (Saito, 1938; also see proceedures in Dartnall, 1957, 1962).

None of the vertebrate visual pigment-complexes are water-soluble; they all require the use of a solubilizing agent to extract them from the retinal rods and cones. Bile salts, sodium cholate, and sodium deoxycholate were the first extractants used in the study of visual pigments. Several synthetic extractants such as cetyltrimethylammonium bromide (CTMAB) and Tergitol NPX have also been used. All of these molecules contain both a hydrophobic and a hydrophilic group, and thus can solubilize material which would otherwise be insoluble. The ionic extractants (the cholates and CTMAB) are believed to function through electrostatic interaction with either the positively charged groups of the protein portion of the visual pigment molecules or with the negatively charged groups.

The most effective extractant (one of the non-ionic detergents) is digitonin, a digitalis glycoside. The specific method of action of this compound is not completely understood. Another extractant that we have used is Tergitol NPX, a monyl phenol polyethylene glycol ether. The hydrophobic part of the molecule is a monyl phenol; the hydrophilic part, an ethylene oxide. The more ether linkages or ethylene oxide groups on the chain, the more centers for hydrogen bonding with water and the greater its solubility.

It is difficult to measure the purity of the extracted rhodopsin, but it has been estimated by the criteria of Wald and Brown (1952), using the ratio of its optical densities, the minimum to that of the maximum absorption (400/500 in mμ). The purer the extract, the lower the ratio, and other indications are obtained from its nitrogen values.

The relative purity of such rhodopsin extracts has been obtained by a comparison of their absorption spectra with the spectral sensitivity curves for the eye (Wald, 1953; Collins, *et al.*, 1952). However, comparison with spectral sensitivity curves in the ultraviolet region can not be made, and the absorption of rhodopsin in this spectral region is assumed to be that of the protein, opsin. Hubbard (1954) estimated the molecular weight of cattle rhodopsin on the assumption that the best extract she obtained with a ratio of mg nitrogen/extinction at 498 mμ was 0.15 and contained rhodopsin and digitonin only.

The separation and extraction of pigments from cattle retinal rods was carried out by the method of Wald and Brown (1952), using 1.8 per cent aqueous digitonin. Other rhodopsin extracts were made with 1.0 per cent aqueous CTMAB and 2 per cent Tergitol NPX.

Rhodopsin fractions with nitrogen values, consistently below the lowest reported by Hubbard (1954), have been obtained from relatively impure extracts by the use of columns of calcium triphosphate gel of 1:1 mixtures of calcium triphosphate and celite (Bowness, 1959).

Chromatography. Columns of calcium triphosphate gel, 1.0 x 6 cm. were prepared by the method of Tiselius, (1954). Columns of calcium triphosphate and celite, 1.0 x 10 cm. were prepared by stirring 10 g. calcium triphosphate, 10 g. celite, and 50 ml. distilled water for thirty minutes. The mixture was poured into a glass column with a sintered filter at the lower end in sufficient amount to give the required length of adsorbent; the upper part of the inner wall was rinsed down with distilled water, and the column allowed to stand for three hours. The excess water was forced through the column.

In chromatograms A and D, (Table IV) the digitonin extracts of retinal rods, after centrifuging at 12,000 rpm for twenty minutes, were diluted with 2 vol. of distilled water and applied to the column with positive pressure from an airline. In chromatogram B, the digitonin extract was diluted with 4 vol. of 0.01 M phosphate buffer pH 7.3 before applying to the column. In chromatogram C, the digitonin extract was diluted with 4 vol. of 0.01 M borate-boric acid buffer, pH 8.1

Elution from the Column. In chromatogram A, material was eluted from the column using 1.4 per cent digitonin in 0.02 M phosphate buffer, pH 7.0. In chromatogram B, material was eluted using 1.8 per cent digitonin in 0.02 M phosphate buffer, pH 6.85. In chromatograms C and D, material was eluted using 1.4 per cent digitonin in 0.02 M phosphate buffer, pH 6.9.

The principal findings for chromatograms with digitonin are shown in Table IV and in Figure 19, the absorption spectrum for a "best" fraction of cattle rhodopsin. A number of chromatograms with rhodopsin preparations not shown in Table IV gave values for the extinction (E 400/498) of the best fractions from these chromatograms from 0.20 (Fig. 19) to 0.28, and values for E 278/498 from 186 to 2.17 (Bowness, 1959).

The recovery of rhodopsin in the effluent fractions, which showed a peak at or near 498 mμ, was 60-80 per cent as estimated by comparing the sum of the absorption readings of the effluent at 498 mμ

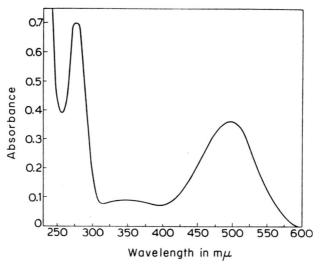

Figure 19 Absorption spectrum of cattle rhodopsin chromatographed from column of calcium triphosphate and celite.

with that of the original extract. These estimated recoveries are probably less than the actual recoveries because a part of the absorption reading at 498 mμ for the original extract is almost certainly due to impurities not present in the effluent fractions.

The "bleaching properties" of rhodopsin were unaltered by passage through the columns under the described conditions. In a typical experiment, an effluent fraction (7-9 ml., pH 6.95) was bleached for twenty minutes with strong white light from a flourescent tube. There was then a peak at 375 mμ and no trace of the peak at 498 mμ. After five hours in the dark, there was 40 per cent regeneration as measured by the absorption value at 498 mμ.

The figures in Table IV show that considerable quantities of nitrogenous impurities may be removed from rhodopsin-containing extracts of retinal rods by using columns containing calcium triphosphate. The nitrogen figures (mg. N for E 498 $=$ 1.0) of the best fractions for the four chromatograms in Table IV group themselves about a mean of 0.148 with a maximum variation of 4 per cent. There is still no certainty that this value is true for pure rhodopsin. The fact that different adsorption and elution procedures yield best fractions with so little variation in their nitrogen contents indicates

TABLE IV
FRACTIONATION OF RHODOPSIN EXTRACTS

Chromatogram and Adsorbent	Fraction Number*	Effluent (ml.)	E 400/498	E 278/498	mg.N for E 498 = 1.0	mg.N for E 278 = 1.0
A Calcium triphosphate and celite	Whole extract		0.310	3.12	0.279	0.089
	1	3-6	0.240	2.50	0.159	0.064
	2	6-9	0.225	2.05	0.152	0.074
	3	9-12	0.278	2.29	0.229	0.100
	4	12-15	0.295	2.98	0.224	0.075
B Calcium triphosphate and celite	Whole extract		0.325	3.41	0.288	0.084
	1	0-2.5	0.520	2.86	0.185	0.065
	2	2.5 -4.5	0.242	2.05	0.142	0.069
	3	4.5 -6.5	0.312	2.41	0.171	0.071
	4	6.5 -8.5	0.311	2.98	0.246	0.083
C Calcium triphosphate and celite	Whole extract		0.384	3.21	0.312	0.097
	1	3-5	0.233	1.91	0.149	0.078
	2	5-7	0.289	2.38	0.165	0.070
	3	7-9	0.327	2.61	0.195	0.075
	4	9-11	0.461	2.93	0.188	0.064
D Calcium triphosphate gel.	Whole extract		0.341	3.10	0.285	0.092
	1	0-2.5	0.380	2.72	0.226	0.083
	2	2.5 -4.5	0.300	2.20	0.192	0.087
	3	4.5 -6.5	0.251	1.89	0.158	0.084
	4	6.5 -8.5	0.245	1.90	0.150	0.079
	5	8.5-10.5	0.310	2.52	0.189	0.075

*Fraction I in each case was the first in which a peak at about 500 mμ was evident.

that this is close to the minimum which can be obtained for rhodopsin in complex with digitonin. The fact that there is no complete separation of fractions on the column does mean that the figure of 0.148 may still be slightly higher than that for a pure fraction, but it seems likely that the value of 0.15 used by Hubbard (1954) in estimating the molecular weight of cattle rhodopsin is very close to the correct one.

The mean of 1.98 of the E 278/498 ratios for the best fractions in Table IV agrees well with the lowest value reported by Albrecht (1957). The maximum variation from this mean was less than 10 per cent. The mean of 0.236 for E 400/498 differed from the extreme figure for other chromatograms of the present work by 18 percent. It is possible either that differences in the amount of non-nitrogenous impurities extracted may be responsible for differences in the E 400/498 ratio or that different solvent solutions affect the light-absorbing properties of rhodopsin differently.

This procedure was also used to separate chicken rhodopsin. However, only partial separation of the cone pigment, iodopsin, was achieved as identified by its absorption spectra from the eluted fractions.

Preparations of rhodopsin can also be made by sonicating the retinal rods at 20,000 cps. for ten to fifteen minutes in the cold and then fractionating the particles in a density gradient tube by centrifugation and ultracentrifugation at 50,470 r.p.m. for one-half hour. Those particles whose spectra showed that they contained rhodopsin were further purified by extraction with petroleum ether and lyophilized to a red powder. The rhodopsin powders can be easily put into solution, (e.g., in 1 per cent aqueous digitonin, 2 per cent aqueous tergitol, NPX, or other detergents). Examples of these extracts are shown in the absorption spectrums, curve 1 of Figure 20, of frog rhodopsin and its light-bleaching curves 2-7, and in curve 1 of Figure 21, cattle rhodopsin and its light-bleaching curves 2-11.

RETINENE-OPSIN COMPLEX

It is visualized that the rhodopsin complex is formed as indicated in Figure 22. The nature of the chemical bond between the chromophore retinene (prosthetic group) of the visual complex and the

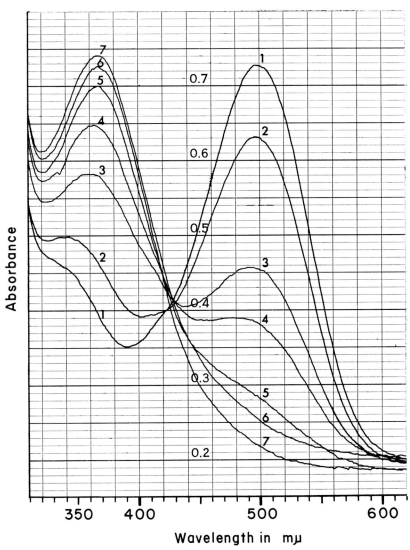

Figure 20 Absorption spectrum of frog rhodopsin, curve 1, and bleaching spectra, curves 2-7.

protein, opsin, is not completely known. Such a complex must be labile to light and must shift the absorption maximum of retinene$_1$ from around 380 mμ in the free state to a much higher absorption near 500 mμ when the retinene is bound with opsin to form rhodopsin.

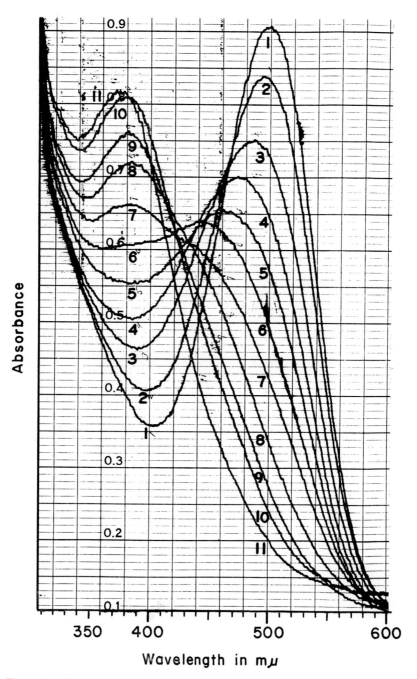

Figure 21 Absorption spectrum of cattle rhodopsin (in 2% equeous tergitol NPX), curve 1, and bleaching spectra curves 2-11.

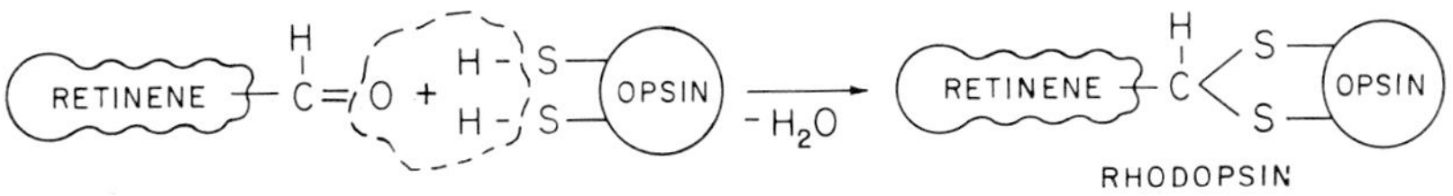

Figure 22 Schematic of the coupling of retinene with opsin to form rhodopsin.

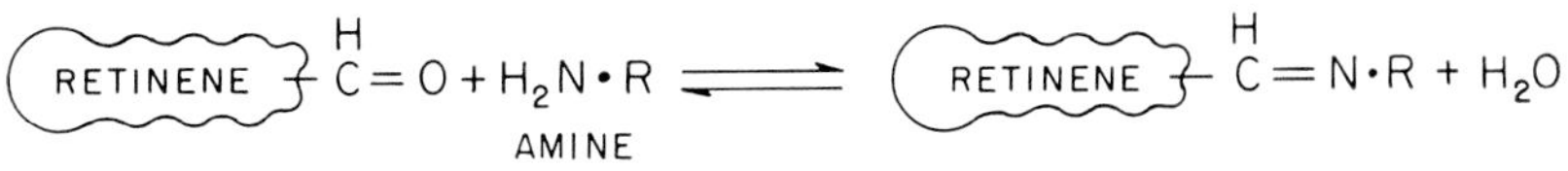

Figure 23 Schematic of the retinene-amine.

An important advance toward the elucidation of the nature of the retinene-protein bond in the visual pigments was the discovery that the retinene$_1$-opsin of rhodopsin is in a Schiff-base linkage with any number of aliphatic amino compounds. Ball *et al* (1949) and Morton and Collins (1950a, b, c) have shown that in rhodopsin, retinene is attached to an amino group as a Schiff-base. Morton and co-workers have further explored the spectroscopic properties of Schiff bases of retinene$_1$ and retinene$_2$ with a variety of amino acids and amines. The reaction involves the condensation of the aldehyde group of retinene with the amino group of amines of amino acids with the elimination of a molecule of H_2O, as schematically illustrated in Figures 22 and 23.

Such Schiff bases (retinene + aliphatic amino compounds) exhibit the same acid-base indicator properties as one of the intermediates in the bleaching of rhodopsin, e.g., 440 mμ "indicator yellow." Shifts in spectra greater than 440 mμ have been attributed by Blatz (1965) to the formation of a stable carbonium ion. Polyenes that are protonated or add Lewis acids in this manner undergo substantial red shifts.

Retinene$_1$ when combined with various proteins, does form complexes some with light-sensitive properties. We have formed such a complex using the all-trans retinene$_1$ by dissolving it in acetone or ethanol and then shaking it with a variety of proteins (solubilized in phosphate buffer or physiological saline). In those reactions in which precipitation occurs, the spectral properties of the dissolved precipitate were investigated. For example, the reaction with albumen does not give a colored precipitate. It was suggested that the protein of rhodopsin was probably a globulin (Broda, 1941). With γ-globulin or horse serum, a precipitate is formed which is colored a deep orange. When these orange precipitates were washed with cold water and centrifuged to remove the excess acetone, dried, and re-extracted with phosphate buffered 1.8 per cent digitonin, pH 6.8, clear orange fractions were obtained which have maximum absorption at 410 mμ. The retinene γ-globulin fraction was found to be soluble in 0.9 NaCl, and when exposed to light immediately bleached from 410 mμ to 385 mμ, as shown in Figure 24.

What this really means is not completely understood. These are not real model systems of the rhodopsin complex, but they may be able to tell us how such pigment-protein complexes affect their spectral properties.

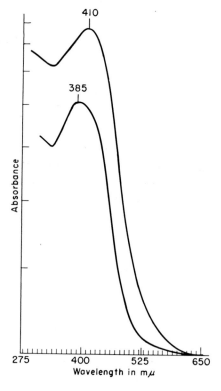

Figure 24 Absorption spectra of retinene₁ γ-globulin complex, λ max. 410 mμ, and bleached spectrum λ max. 385 mμ.

Histological methods have been used in attempts to find enzymatic activity in the rod outer segment membrane and further clues to the nature of opsin. Histochemical evidence indicates that a nucleoside triphosphatase is present in the membranes of the outer segments of frog retinal receptors. Rhodopsin extracts (in digitonin) exhibit more substantial adenosine triphosphatase (ATPase) activity in bright light than in darkness. All enzyme activity is eliminated by hydroxylamine, which traps retinene to form a retinene-oxime releasing opsin.

When solutions of frog or cattle opsin are incubated with a solution of all-trans retinene$_1$, the activity of the enzyme increases with rhodopsin formation by evidence of its maximum absorption peak. From these experiments, McConnell and Scarpelli (1963) indicate that rhodopsin is an adenosine triphosphatase (ATPase) which requires the attachment of its retinene chromophore for activity. In this way, retinene may act as a light trap and also as a co-factor for the enzyme. Goldsmith has found that the ATPase activity of dark-adapted rods is insensitive to light, and that after extraction with 2 per cent aqueous digitonin, the residue contains no more than 4 per cent ATPase activity and no rhodopsin. He, therefore, concludes that the ATPase activity is not the property of the visual pigment.

It is interesting here to point out something of the cytochrome system, for, as indicated by Hill and Bendall (1960), mitochondria and chloroplasts show some resemblance to their structure-bound cytochromes. The chloroplasts (and possibly the inner retinal rod segments) belong to the same category as the mitochondria, where the a-component of the cytochrome system is replaced by the chlorophylls in the chloroplast. It would be interesting to know more of the cytochrome system of the inner segments of the retinal rods and whether or not retinene replaces one of the cytochrome components in the retinal rods. These cytochromes isolated from the chloroplasts, however, have not been identified in the retinal rods. (Wolken and Gross 1963) Before concluding this discussion, the occurrence of the ultraviolet sensitivity of visual receptors should be indicated (Wald and Krainin, 1963). These considerations may also apply to *Aphakics*. Their ultraviolet sensitivity is remarkable; acuity is retained at 365 mμ and vision to 309 mμ is claimed (Wald, 1945). Also, the absorption maxima of the responses of insects are so close to the absorption peak of alcohol dehydrogenase, DPNH, in cells that Chance (1964) describes on this basis an experiment that shows that the fluorescence of mitochondrial DPNH can provide by energy transfer, a system suitable for causing photochemical reactions in cells. A higher sensitivity toward ultraviolet radiation has been found in mitochondrial suspensions and intact cells which contain DPNH than that which has been observed in purified cytochrome oxidase (free of DPNH). Chance's experiments (Chance and Baltscheffsky, 1958) seem consistent with the view that excitation of fluorescence of mitochondrial DPNH (λ max 340 mμ) provides a highly efficient fluorescence emission in the region of 410-500 mμ (λ max 443 mμ). This fluorescence intensity is apparently sufficient to accelerate the photodecomposition of the CO compound of cytochrome oxidase.

The different time dependence of the electroretinograms (Wald and Krainin, 1963; Goldsmith and Ruck, 1958) may reflect an activation of mitochondrial function by the visual response itself. It has been speculated that such energy loads of the visual response are supplied by these mitochondria, and that rapid changes of the oxidation reduction state of the DPNH may be involved in such responses as has been observed in muscular contractions (Chance and Jöbsis, 1959).

Chance's observations on cytochrome a_3 photodisassociation and on visual sensitivity call attention to the facts that mitochondrial DPNH is a natural fluorescence of aerobic tissues and that its fluorescence is readily excited by radiation in the region from 370 mμ to 310 mμ for the nicotenimide and at even shorter wavelengths from the adenine group or from the aromatic amino acid groups of the binding protein. All of these considerations indicate that we need to obtain more biochemical information on the protein and enzyme systems of the retinal rods and cones.

Molecular Weight

It is difficult to measure accurately the molecular weight of rhodopsin, since the extracted rhodopsin is a complex (in the digitonin micelles). It is possible, however, to obtain from rhodopsin the absorption spectra, the concentration, the dried weight, and the nitrogen. From these data and its sedimentation (obtained from studies in the analytical ultracentrifuge), an estimate of the molecular weight rhodopsin can be made.

Because of the questionable criteria of the purity of the rhodopsin (cattle, frog), our experimental values may be distorted by both low nitrogens and high dry weights (i.e., the weight is high with respect to the pigment concentration).

Digitonin, used to extract the rhodopsin, forms micelles in solution from its sedimentation (7.1 in Svedburg units, see Table V), a minimum molecular weight of 75,000 was calculated. It was estimated that three such micelles are aggregated to form a molecular weight of 225,000 (Hubbard, 1954). Frog rhodopsin (in digitonin) sediments with a single boundary (Fig. 25) and a sedimentation con-

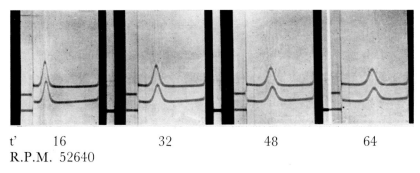

t'   16   32   48   64
R.P.M. 52640

Figure 25 Dual sedimentation diagram from the analytical ultracentrifuge. Frog rhodopsin (in 1.8% digitonin) for various time intervals to 64 minutes run at 52,640 rpm.

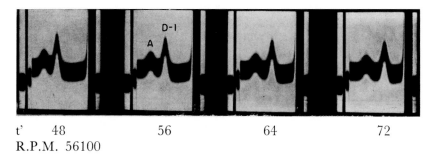

t'   48   56   64   72
R.P.M. 56100

Figure 26 Sedimentation of digitonin (D-1) mixed with bovine albumin (A) for various time intervals to 64 minutes run at 56,100 rpm.

stant of 12.1 (Wolken, 1956a), while cattle rhodopsin, similarly
prepared, also sediments with a single boundary and has a sedimentation constant of 9.77 (Hubbard, 1954). When the cattle rhodopsin-
digitonin complex was diluted with additional digitonin solution,
Hubbard (1954) found two distinct boundaries formed upon sedimentation; one corresponding to the rhodopsin-digitonin complex,
and the other to the free digitonin micelles. However, no complex
is formed when digitonin and albumin are mixed, and both sediment as separate entities (Fig. 26). What specificity digitonin has
for certain proteins or for the protein or lipoprotein of the rhodopsin
molecule in the complex is not known. An estimate of the molecular
weight of rhodopsin was calculated using the rhodopsin sedimentation constant (S_{20}) from the Svedburg equation:

$$M = \frac{RTS_{20}}{D_{20} (1 - p\overline{V}_{20})}$$

where R is the gas constant, 8.32×10^7 dynes/cm; T is the absolute
temperature; S_{20} the experimentally determined sedimentation; D_{20}
the diffusion constant of digitonin, 4×10^{-7}; $\overline{V}_{20}$ the partial specific
volume, 0.738; p the density of the protein, 1.3 (or if a lipoprotein
1.1). This gives values for the rhodopsin complex-micelle weight of
275,000 for cattle rhodopsin and 295,000 for frog rhodopsin (Table
V).

Using the analytical data in Tables V and VI, the molecular
weight for frog rhodopsin can also be estimated from

$$M = \frac{w' (100)}{P (15)}$$

where M is the molecular weight of the rhodopsin macromolecule;
w' is the weight of nitrogen in milligrams associated with 1 ml. of
the extract; and P is the pigment concentration in moles per liter
of extract.

The estimated molecular weight for frog rhodopsin on this basis
is 67,000, and for cattle rhodopsin, 40,000. A molecular weight of
40,000 for cattle rhodopsin was also calculated by Hubbard (1954).
If, in calculating M, the density of a lipoprotein (1.1) is taken, it
would reduce the molecular weight by 20 per cent and result in a
molecular weight of 32,000 for cattle rhodopsin and 54,000 for frog
rhodopsin.

It has been demonstrated that one retinene molecule is most probably associated with one opsin molecule in rhodopsin (Wolken, 1956a, 1962b). The possibility that there may be more than one retinene molecule per rhodopsin molecule cannot, however, be excluded.

TABLE V

RHODOPSIN
ANALYTICAL ULTRACENRIFUGE DATA

Pigment complex in digitonin	Average sedimentation $S_{20} \times 10^{13}$	Average complex micelle weight M^1	Average calculated molecular weight M
Digitonin[+]	7.10	155,000[+]	————
Cattle rhodopsin	9.77	275,000	40,000
Frog rhodopsin	12.10	295,000	67,000

[+] Minimum weight of digitonin micelle, estimated to be 75,000 (Hubbard, 1954). M is calculated from M^1 using the dry weights and per cent nitrogen (Wolken, 1961a).

TABLE VI

ANALYSIS OF FROG RHODOPSIN
(Rana pipiens)

	1	2
w mg/ml dry weight	21.0	20.0
w' mg/ml N	0.033	0.026
w" mg/ml digitonin	13.2	15.0
P moles/liter rhodopsin pigment	3.2×10^{-6}	2.2×10^{-6}

Chapter V

THE RETINA

THE STRUCTURE AND SPECTRAL SENSITIVITY OF
RODS AND CONES

THE MORPHOLOGY OF the rods and cones was described, in a general way, by Schultz in 1866, who fixed the retinas in osmium tetroxide (OsO_4) and examined their structure. He also observed that the retinal rods disintegrate into platelets. This was followed by the studies of Böll in 1876 and Kühne in 1877, who demonstrated the photosensitive nature of the retinal rods; the bleaching of their pigment in the light and its regeneration in the dark. These clues from almost a century ago have been followed by the most modern techniques in microscopy and biochemistry.

The rods and cones are differentiated structures of the retinal cells; each has an inner segment and what appears as a rod or cone-shaped outer segment which contains all of the photosensitive visual pigments. These are illustrated at low magnification for the frog rod in Figures 27 and 28a, and for the cone in Figure 29a.

The refractive index of isolated rods and cones has been estimated by Sidman (1957) using interference phase microscopy. The refractive index for the outer segments of rods in a number of species is about 1.41, and for the cone outer segments about 1.385. The extra-cellular fluid which separates outer segments in the living retina has a refractive index of 1.334, which is very similar to that of physiological saline.

Schmidt (1935, 1937, 1938), using polarizing microscopy, demonstrated that the optical properties of the outer segment closely correspond with those of the myelin sheath of nerve. He suggested that since, from the optical properties, the long axis of the lipoid molecules appears to run parallel to the axis of the outer segment, there must be planes of non-lipoidal material arranged at right angles to the long axis, in order to account for the reversal in sign of

[52]

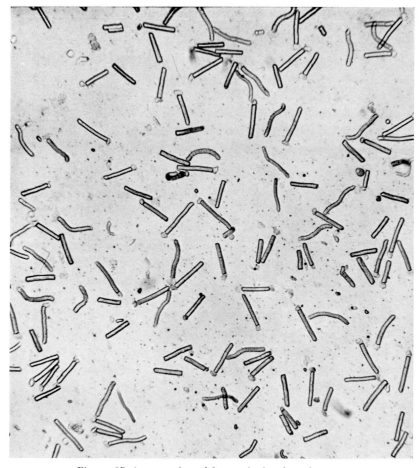

Figure 27 A suspension of frog retinal rods and cones.

birefringence when lipoids are extracted. He then demonstrated that the molecules of the non-lipoidal discs lie transversely to the axis. Treatment with dilute alkali or acids leads not only to a disappearance of the positive birefringence, but also to a transverse shrinkage of the outer segments, accompanied by a lengthening to as much as ten times their original length. Further observations on the dichroism of the outer segments suggested that the visual pigment is probably oriented in the non-lipoidal regions of the retinal rod. With longitudinally sectioned rod-outer-segments freed from lipoid,

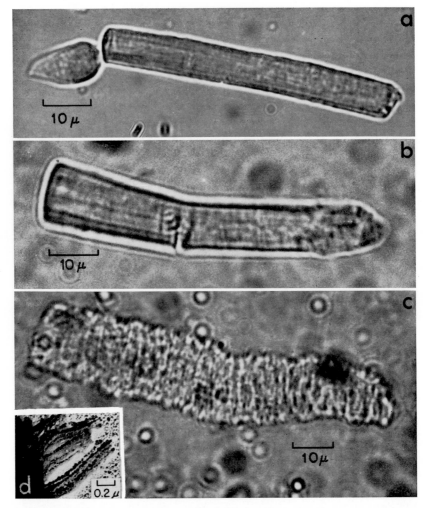

Figure 28a Photomicrograph of an isolated frog rod.
  b and c. Showing structural changes when exposed to white light.
      d. Electron micrograph of whole frog rod fixed 15 minutes in OsO₄
          and shadowed with palladium at an angle of 20°.

Schmidt was able to show a complete curve for birefringence as a function of the refractive index of the medium. The negative uni-axial form birefringence observed is characteristic of a laminated structure, and is consistant with the view that the outer segments

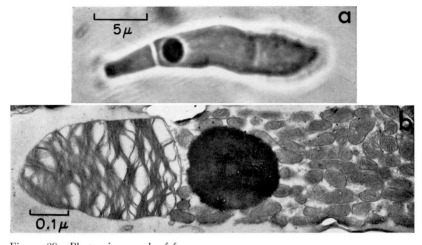

Figure 29a Photomicrograph of frog cone.
     b Electron micrograph of frog cone; note the ellipsoid and mitochondria in the inner segment.

are superimposed platelets. Schematized retinal rod cells are shown in Figure 30 (De Robertis, 1956).

The first electron microscopic studies were of sonicated, fixed, and shadowed guinea pig retinal rod outer segments (Sjöstrand, 1949, 1953a, b). These micrographs clearly showed that they were platelets of about 2μ in diameter, with edges of 75 Å in thickness. These early electron micrographs, electron microscopic studies have revealed that all the vertebrate retinal rod outer segments (e.g., perch, cattle, rabbit, rat, monkey, and man) that have been fixed and stained by various techniques and examined in the electron microscope, show dense, double-membraned lamellae (platelets, discs, sacs) that are of the order of 200 Å in thickness and that are separated by less dense layers 200-500 Å in thickness. Each membrane (lamellae) of the discs is from 50-75 Å in thickness (Cohen, 1961, 1963a, b, 1964; De Robertis, 1956; De Robertis and Lassansky, 1961; Dowling, 1965; Fernández-Morán, 1958, 1959, 1961; Fernández-Morán and Brown, 1958; Missotten, 1964; Sjöstrand, 1953a, b, 1959, 1960, 1961; Wolken, 1956a, 1958a, 1961a, b, 1963).

Electron micrographs of the frog rod (Figs. 31, 32, 33) and the cattle rod (Fig. 34) illustrate the double membrane lamellar struc-

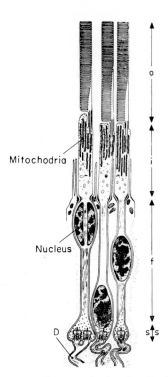

Figure 30 Schematized vertebrate retinal rod cells (De Robertis, 1956).

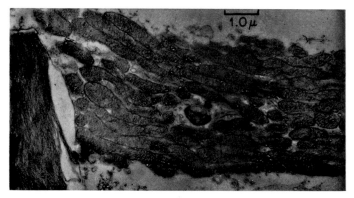

Figure 31 Longitudinal section of inner segment of frog retinal rod.

ture. The cross-sectional view of the frog rod shows a cylinder with scalloped edges and fissures extending into the rod, so that it is divided into fifteen to twenty irregular, pie-shaped wedges (Fig. 32a). Longitudinal sections reveal that these lobes produce further divisions within the structure of the rod (Fig. 32b).

The inner segments are packed mitochondria, as seen in Figures 31 and 33. The outer segment appears to be connected to the inner segment by a continuous membrane. Interconnections are through a fibril (a cilium) that runs from the outer segment through the inner segment (Fig. 33a). Embryologically, the rods and cones are probably derived from flagella, and in this respect it was interesting to observe (De Robertis, 1956) that the base of the outer segment is connected to the distal end of the inner segment by a flagellum. The structure of the flagellum is similar in arrangement to that of the nine fibrils found in the cilia, flagella, and spermatozoa tails of many plant and animal cells (compare Fig. 33a with Fig. 60c). Also, the close association of the mitochondria (the enzyme packages) of the inner segment with the central end of the fiber may be a significant factor in the functional chemistry of the rods and cones.

The frog eye has large retinal rod outer segments (Figs. 27, 28, 31, 32) which ranges to 6μ in diameter and to 60μ in length. With the light microscope, these rods can be observed in the retina, and they can be easily isolated from it (Fig. 27). When viewed in red light, the isolated frog retinal rods (in frog Ringers solution)

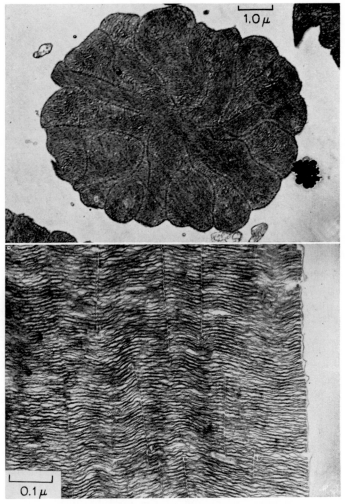

Figure 32 Electron micrographs of frog retinal rod outer segments.
     a. Cross-section of outer segment.
     b. Longitudinal section of outer segment showing *fine structure*.

appear highly refractive and seem to be constructed of long, packed rods of about 1μ in diameter. As soon as white light is turned on, the entire outer segment swells, and, as if subject to osmotic shock, begins to break transversely rather than longitudinally, so that within a few minutes all structural identity is destroyed (Wolken

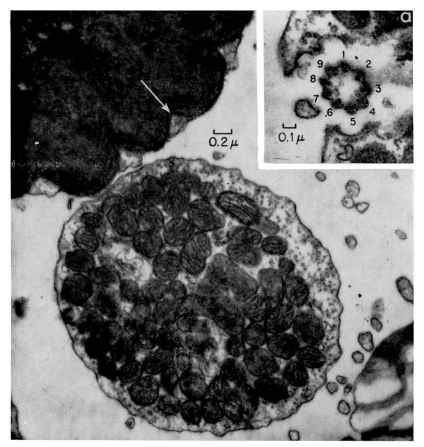

Figure 33 Section through frog retinal rod showing connection and structure
between outer segment and inner segment. Note dendritic-like structures between the lobes in the outer segment.
a. Structure of fibril (cilium) that penetrates from the outer segment
through the inner segment.

1961a). This change in morphology indicates that most of the visual
pigment is bleached. This sequence of events is illustrated in Figure 28.

When freshly excised retinas or their isolated retinal rods and
cones are immediately fixed in the cold with 1 per cent osmium
tetroxide (in phosphate buffer), embedded, thin-sectioned, and observed in the electron microscope, the *fine structure* details as described for these rods (Figs. 31, 32 and 33) become very apparent.

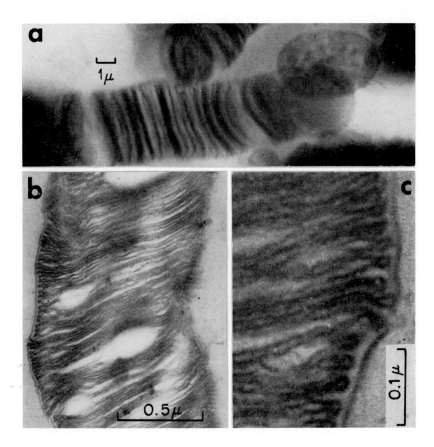

Figure 34 Cattle retinal rods; electron micrographs.
  a. Rod outer segment, osmotically shocked. Note separation of plates.
  b. Longitudinal section.
  c. Longitudinal section at high resolution.

Strong white light (400 foot-candles) destroys this ordered lamellar structure (Fig. 35). When the rods are light bleached for fifteen minutes in the presence of hydroxylamine, the trapping agent for retinene, a disordered array of various sized, double-membraned platelets is found (Fig. 36). The size of the platelets appears to be due to the separation of the lamellae at the fissure joints. It therefore seems that the organized structure is concentration de-

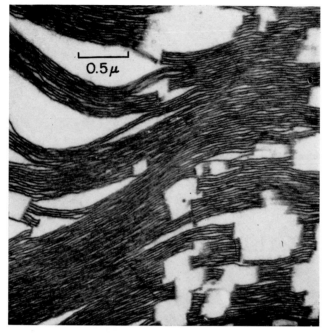

Figure 35 Light bleached frog rod; electron micrograph.

pendent on retinene to form the visual complex and that the rod structure can be destroyed, not only by chemical removal of retinene from the visual complex in the rods, but also by physical means, light or heat.

Spectroscopy of Retinal Rods and Cones

The extraction of the visual pigments from the retinal tissue cells is an arduous task, for it requires a large number of animal eyes, dissection, fractionation, solubilization, and hours of preparation in the dark and in the cold. To circumvent these procedures and chemical processing and to obtain more useful information on the visual pigments in their natural state, microspectrophotometry has been applied to identify them in single retinal rods and cones and during light $<$---$>$dark reactions (Brown, 1961; Hanaoka and Fujimoto, 1957; Liebman, 1962; Strother and Wolken, 1959; Wolken and Strother, 1963; Marks, 1963; Liebman and Entine, 1964).

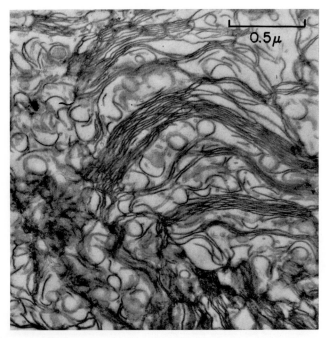

Figure 36 Hydroxylamine bleached frog rod; electron micrograph.

Spectrophotometric data obtained from extracts of retinal rods and measurements of their spectral sensitivity have led to the conclusion that rhodopsin is the light-absorbing pigment responsible for the "primary event" in visual excitation. Granit (1955), however, suggested that it was premature to assume, from the facts emerging from extraction of the visual pigments by detergents, that the broadband rhodopsin absorption curves are the only photochemically active substances found in the rods. Comparison of the absorption spectral data of rhodopsin and that of the *in situ* retinal rods should reveal information relative to the nature of the photosensitive visual pigment. In addition, it should show whether there is *fine structure* in the spectra of individual rods that is not observed for the extracted visual pigments in solution.

Retinas were removed from dark-adapted eyes of frogs, chickens, cattle, and humans. They were then agitated to isolate the rods from the pigment epithelium. The free rods were placed in a drop of frog Ringers or physiological saline (0.9 per cent NaCl) solution on a miroscope slide, with a cover glass that was sealed with petrolatum and a slight pressure to prevent evaporation and movement of the rods. All operations, including the preparation, focus, and location of the rod, were carried out in dim red light within ten minutes after dissection (Wolken, 1962a).

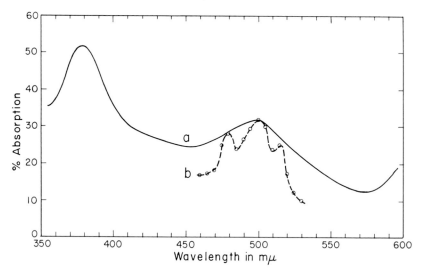

Figure 37a Absorption spectrum of frog rhodopsin.
    b. Absorption spectrum at 5 mμ intervals from 460 to 530 mμ.

The retina of the frog contains about 50 per cent rods that appear to be "red" and about 8 per cent "green" rods (Denton and Wyllie, 1955). An absorption spectrum for frog rhodopsin, Fig. 37 curve a, is compared to a spectrum of a frog rod which shows absorption peaks at 480, 500, and 515 mμ (Fig. 37 curve b) and has peaks at 280, 340, 355, and 380 mμ in the ultraviolet. Upon bleaching with strong white light until the rod shows signs of transverse striations (Fig. 28b, c, d), the 380 mμ absorption peak is substantially increased. Since the rods are very photosensitive, any exposure during the process of taking the absorption spectrum results in some bleaching. More than 100 individual frog rods were scanned at each wavelength with the micro-spectrophotometer to construct the composite spectrum (Fig. 38a). Its similarity to the absorption curve of extracted rhodopsin (Fig. 38b) is unmistakable. The large average deviation in the region of

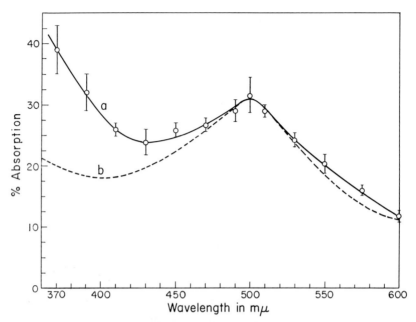

Figure 38a Absorption spectrum, composite of 100 frog rods in which the data
          for each rod is taken at only one wave length.
      b. Rhodopsin spectrum.

380 mμ indicates that a variation in the amount of vitamin A and/or
retinene is present in the *in situ* rod. Observe in Fig. 39a the absorption curve of a frog rod and the hydroxylamine (NH_2OH) bleached
rod Fig. 39b. Fig. 39c is a rod from a light-adapted retina and shows
a shift to about 490 mμ, possibly isorhodopsin (λ max at 490 $\pm$ 2
mμ). The difference spectrum is nearly identical to those recorded
for extracted rhodopsin (Dartnall, 1957). Compare these data to
that of the rhodopsin bleaching scheme of Dartnall (Table VII).

    Recorded absorption spectra using the microspectrophotometer, of
single frog retinal rods show a peak near 498 $\pm$ 5 mμ for "red" rods
(Fig. 40 curve a). Upon bleaching with light at 500 mμ (Fig. 40
curves b, c, and d), the 498 mμ peak decreases and the 380 mμ
increases as already noted in Fig. 39b and c. Absorption spectra
of frog rods also obtained by microspectrophotometry by Brown
(1961) and Liebman (1962) show similar spectra.

    The results of a sweep at 500 mμ at intervals of 0.5μ along the

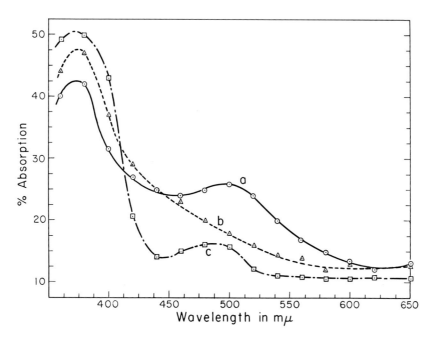

Figure 39a Absorption spectrum of frog rod.
　　　　b. Absorption spectrum of frog rod after bleaching with white light in
　　　　the presence of NH$_2$OH.
　　　　c. Absorption spectrum of a frog rod from the eye of a light adapted
　　　　　　　frog.

length and width of the rod, indicate that rhodopsin is distributed
evenly throughout the outer segment (Fig. 41) and as visualized
in Fig. 89 our retinal rod model (Wolken, 1961a). Knowing the
volume of the retinal rod, its absorption maximum at 500 mμ, and
the molar extinction coefficient, an estimate of the number of rhodopsin molecules can be calculated. From our data this is 3×10^9
molecules per frog retinal rod, which is in agreement with measurements for frog rhodopsin.

The "green" frog rods, which are more difficult to identify (Denton
and Wyllie, 1955), show spectra with peaks at 460 to 470 mμ,
530 to 540 mμ, and a maximum at 610 mμ, which appears to be
in agreement with the data of Granit (1955) and Arden (1954).

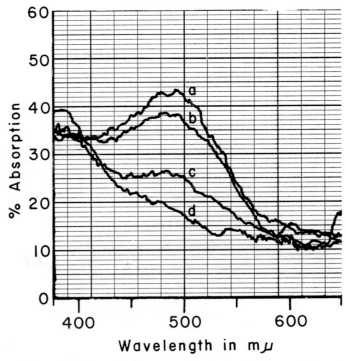

Figure 40 Recorded absorption spectra of single *in situ* frog retinal rod (curve a); bleached at 500 mμ and spectra recorded (curves b, c, and d). Time of scan 2 minutes; halfband width 3 mμ.

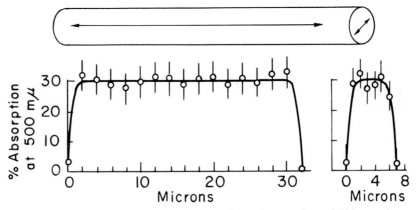

Figure 41 Scans of a frog retinal rod at its absorption maxima of 500 mμ along its length and width.

TABLE VII

PRODUCTS WHICH MAY BE FORMED ON BLEACHING RHODOPSIN*

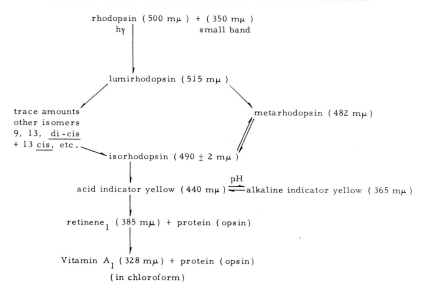

rhodopsin (500 mμ) + (350 mμ)
hγ   small band

lumirhodopsin (515 mμ)

trace amounts   metarhodopsin (482 mμ)
other isomers
9, 13, di - cis
+ 13 cis, etc.

isorhodopsin (490 ± 2 mμ)

                                    pH
acid indicator yellow (440 mμ) ⇌ alkaline indicator yellow (365 mμ)

retinene₁ (385 mμ) + protein (opsin)

Vitamin A₁ (328 mμ) + protein (opsin)
(in chloroform)

---

*No attempt is made here to distinguish between photo, thermal, or enzymatic bleaching. The absorption peaks and products were taken in part from Dartnall (1957, p. 54).

SPECTRAL SENSITIVITY OF CONES AND COLOR VISION

How the human eye resolves color is not known. The two general theories of color vision are the *tricolor theory,* which arose from the works of Young (1802, 1807), Helmholtz (1852, 1867) and Maxwell (1861 and 1890), and the theory of Hering (1885, 1925, 1965, trans. by Hurvich and Jameson). The tricolor theory assumes that there are three pigments in the different retinal cones with maximum absorption in the *blue, green,* and *red* regions, respectively. According to this theory, the brain "computes" yellow and white from green and red at high luminosities, and white from blue at low luminosities. In two most common forms of color blindness, *red,* Protanopia, and *green,* Deuteranopia, cannot be discriminated, but yellow is experienced. Hering's theory postulated that there are six responses occurring in pairs. Excitation leading to any single response suppresses the action of the other member of the pair.

These six responses are identified as blue-yellow, red-green, and black-white.

These theories were originally based almost exclusively on psychophysical evidence. Other data is now becoming available from the cone structure, pigment photochemistry, electrophysiology, and communication theory (Muturana et al 1960) that must be considered before a complete theory of color vision can be established.

The simplest assumption is that human cones contain three different light-sensitive pigments, although only one photosensitive cone pigment either iodopsin or cyanopsin has been identified, (Figs. 16 and 17). The cones are fewer in number, smaller in size, and much more photosensitive than the retinal rods. They are also difficult to isolate and to extract chemically. However, they can be isolated microscopically in suspensions with the rods, and their absorption spectra obtained in a manner very similar to that used for the rods (Wolken, 1962a). For frog cones there is general absorption throughout the whole of the visible spectrum and absorption peaks near 430, 480, 540, 610, and 680 mμ were observed (Wolken, 1963). Since the cones appear to disintegrate more rapidly than the rods, many of these peaks could be products of bleaching. Liebman, however, indicates that frog cones have only one absorption peak at 570 $\pm$ 10 mμ. It is of interest to compare these peaks with those for the carp cone (Hanaoka and Fujimoto, 1957), in which peaks in the regions of 420-430, 490-500, 520-540, 560-580, 620-640, and 670-680 were found. In the goldfish, which belongs to the carp family, Marks (1963) found cones with absorption peaks at 455, 530, and 624 mμ. Liebman and Entine (1964) found different absorption peaks for the goldfish cones at 460, 540, and 640 mμ (see Fig. 42). These compare closely to the photopic spectral sensitivity curves of Granit (1955) and Weale (1960) as measured in the living eye. Rushton (1958, 1962) using reflection densitometry, detected at least two absorbing pigments in the living human fovea of the retina; one absorbing at 540 mμ and the other at 590 mμ. Brown and Wald (1963, 1964), using microspectrophotometry, also detected pigments absorbing at 535 and 565 mμ in human foveal cones, and for monkey foveal cones absorption peaks at 527 and 565 were found. Marks, Dobelle, and MacNichol (1964) and MacNichol (1964) also using microspectrophotometric methods, recorded absorption peaks for human and monkey cones at 445, 535, and 570 mμ. Wald (1964) has since found, for the human cones, absorption peaks at

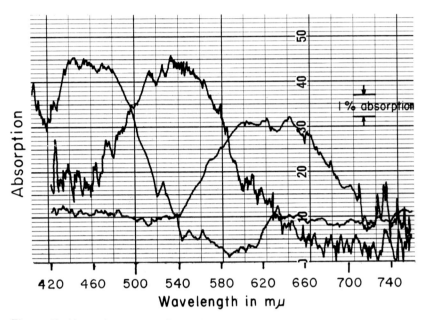

Figure 42 Absorption spectra obtained from three different cones from the goldfish (from Liebman and Entine, 1964).

450, 525, and 555 mμ which he has compared to his psychophysical data of the human eye that has major absorption peaks at 430, 540, and 575 mμ.

These recent studies indicate that color vision in vertebrates is probably mediated by three different light-sensitive pigments in different receptors; one for sensing blue—one for green—and one for red.

There is no real proof that there are no more than three different cone absorbing pigments for one animal. Our own data indicates that there could be more than three different absorption peaks for the frog cones. As our instrumentation becomes more refined, we shall be able to learn more of the biochemistry of the retinal pigments in their living state. However, the absorption spectral data of the pigment complexes within a single rod or cone can now begin to be compared to the spectral sensitivity curves of the living eye and to the chemistry of the extracted visual pigment-complexes in solution.

Oil Globules

In the cones of some animals, e.g., birds, amphibians, lizards, and snakes, there is a system of colored oil globules (Figs. 43 and 44). These globules evolved a long way back, since they are found in the retinas of ancient fish, *Chrondrosteans* and sturgeons, but modern fish, with the exception of the lungfish, have discarded them. The globules are situated between the inner and outer segments of the cone, so that light must pass through them before entering the photosensitive pigments in the outer segment. The globules, however, are in a position to act as color filters, but what function they have in the retina and in vision, particularly color vision, is still unknown. It was suggested nearly a hundred years ago that the oil globules, by differentially transmitting light to the outer segments

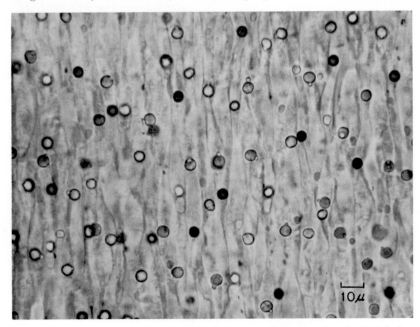

Figure 43 Chicken retina, freshly excised, showing different colored oil globules; note density of these colored oil globules.

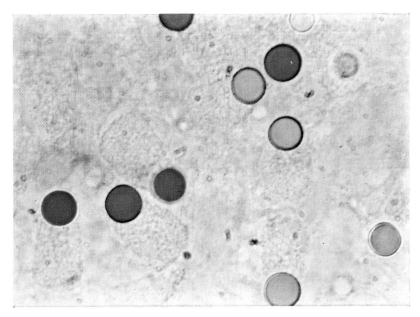

Figure 44 Color photomicrograph of the oil globules of swamp turtle *(Pseudemys scripta elegans)*.

affect the spectral response of the cone, and thus can provide the basis of color differentiation in the animals possessing them.

The ophthalmologist, Siegfried Garten, published a paper in Germany, in 1907, indicating a system of color photography based upon this principle. The French chemist, Louis Lumiérè, without benefit of chicken retinas, brought out an autochrome process for color photography in 1906 (in Wallon 1921). Lumiérè used suspensions of starch grains dyed red, green, and blue, mixed in roughly equal proportions and strewn over the surface of an ordinary photographic plate. The granules were squashed flat and the interstices filled with particles of carbon. Each dyed granule served as a color filter for the patch of silver bromide emulsion that lay beneath it.

The chicken, pigeon, and turtle eyes, in whose retinas cones predominate, contain colored oil globules. These animals necessarily function only at high light intensity. In a freshly excised chicken retina, the predominant colors are red, green, and yellow, and the globules range from 3-5μ in diameter. It is possible to isolate the colored globules by flotation when retinal homogenates are centrifuged in phosphate buffer. The globules are considered to be carotenoid-lipid or possibly pigment-lipoprotein complexes. The different colored oil globules have long been suspected of acting as color filters for the retinal cones (Fujimoto *et al.,* 1957; Walls, 1942). Since a red globule absorbs light somewhere in the blue-green region, the location of the globule between the inner cone segment and the light source makes a color theory reasonable. There is no direct correlation, however, between the color of the globule and the color discrimination of the animal possessing it.

A very early *in situ* investigation of these globules indicated the presence of carotenoids. From the chicken retina, Wald and Zussman (1938) obtained three colored extracts in organic solvents, which resembled the colors of the oil globules. Their results showed that these extracts do contain carotenoids, including a new carotenoid named galloxanthin (Wald, 1948).

To obtain the absorption spectra of these colored oil globules, the retinas from freshly killed chickens were removed by dissection under dim red light, placed in 0.05 M phosphate buffer at pH 6.5, and kept in the dark at 4°C. They were prepared for microspectrophotometry by cutting a section about 3 mm.^{2} into smaller areas with a sharp scalpel on a microscope slide. A coverglass was then placed over the retinal material, pressed down firmly, and sealed to retard drying (Strother and Wolken, 1960a). Figure 43 shows a photomicrograph taken of a fresh chicken retina indicating the relative density and size of the globules. (A colored micrograph of the swamp turtle globules is shown in Fig. 44.)

The absorption spectra obtained from the red, yellow, and green globules shows absorption maxima in three different regions of the spectrum, as would be expected from the colors. The absorption does not show sharp peaks, but very broad bands are evident; the width of the band increases as the maximum absorbing wavelength increases. The red oil globules have an absorption maximum from 480-560 mμ; the green globules have a general absorption in the region 390-440 mμ; and the yellow globules have a broad absorption peak in the region 440-480 mμ (Fig 45). When small amounts of antimony trichloride saturated in chloroform were placed on the micro-

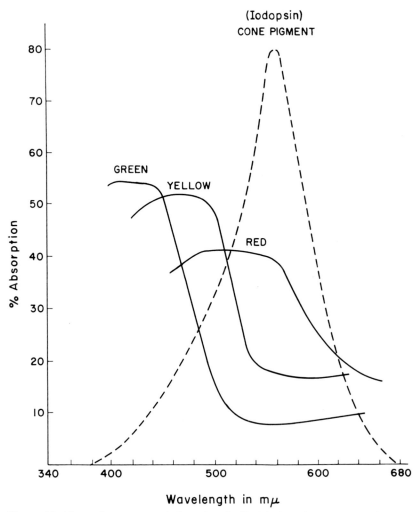

Figure 45 Absorption spectra of the colored oil globules of the chicken, for the red, yellow, and green, compared to the chicken cone pigment, iodopsin (---).

scope slide, the yellow and green globules turned blue, bleaching out slowly upon light exposure. The red globules first turned purple, and then became opaque. The blue color is a characteristic reaction for carotenoids in general; the purple color may be specific for the reaction between astacene and antimony trichloride (Giliam, 1935). The absorption spectrum for the blue globules obtained with antimony trichloride showed a maximum absorption peak at 810 mμ and secondary maxima at 720 and 615 mμ. Vitamin A has not been identified in these globules (Wald, 1948), but these spectra peaks indicate that vitamin A may be present.

The carotenoids, lutein, zeaxanthin, astaxanthin, galloxanthin, and sarcinene, a hydrocarbon, have been extracted from chicken retinas (Wald, 1948; Wald and Zussman, 1938). All of these compounds have different absorption peaks in different solvents; thus an exact tentative identification of the pigments is possible. The green globules have maximum absorption in the blue region of the spectrum, and, although other carotenoids may be present, they appear to be galloxanthin, whose absorption peaks are at 387, 407, and 427 mμ in chloroform (Wald, 1948). The maximum absorption of the yellow globules is in the region 420 to 500 mμ, characteristic of lutein and zeaxanthin. The absorption peak of the red globules is very near 500 mμ, corresponding to astaxanthin, which has a single absorption peak at 502 mμ in carbon disulfide (Wald and Zussman, 1938), although other pigments are associated with absorption maxima near 430 and 560 mμ. The spectrum of the blue globules corresponds in general with the spectrum of the lutein-antimony trichloride reaction, which has a peak at 617 mμ, an inflection at 580-590 mμ, and strong absorption in the red beyond 700 mμ (Giliam, 1935).

Qualitative observations on bleaching indicate that the green globules are the most unstable of the three. After a thirty minute exposure to monchromatic light over the range 340 to 700 mμ, the height of their absorption peak decreased by about 15 per cent. After a retinal sample is stored in the dark at 4°C., many of the green globules turn colorless. When all the globules are mixed together, a reddish-orange color results, which, when exposed to white light bleaches first to orange, then yellow, then colorless.

Absorption in the 350-280 mμ region is characteristic of many types of chromophoric groups, including long chain unsaturated fatty acids (Brode, 1943). All the oil globule mixtures investigated in the ultraviolet region began to fluoresce at about 270 mμ, as noted by a sharp cut-off in absorption, to a value less than zero at a wavelength of 250 mμ. The data also indicate that absorption in the ultraviolet region below 310 mμ is greater than that in the visible region.

Carotenoids are usually described as non-fluorescent, although a few exceptions (i.e., phytofluene) have been noted (Rabinowitch, 1951). High absorption for the globule mixture in the ultraviolet region is not characteristic of carotenoids (Karrer and Jucker, 1950). Characteristic absorption for proteins in the ultraviolet region is near 270 mμ (Beaven and Holiday, 1952). The presence of chromophoric groups with absorption peaks at 330 mμ and below is indicated, however, as well as the presence of lipids. If one assumes that the globules are acting merely as color filters, then the green and yellow globules are relatively inefficient, since the chicken cone pigment, iodopsin (Fig. 45), has a single absorption peak at 550 mμ (Hubbard and Kropf, 1959a). Only the red globule has appreciable absorption in this region.

Strother (1963) investigated the colored oil globules for the American Bronze turkey, swamp turtle *(Pseudemys elegans)*, wood turtle *(Clemmys insculpa)*, and domestic white pigeon. His results show that there is about 80 per cent absorption of light regardless of

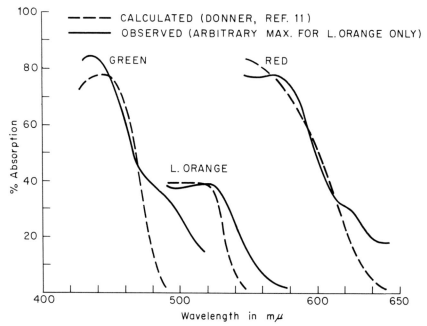

Figure 46 Comparison between calculated and observed pigeon oil globule spectra (- - -, calculated) and (——, observed), from Strother, 1963.

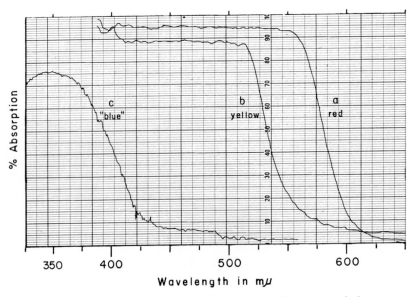

Figure 47 Absorption spectra of individual colored oil globules of the swamp turtle (*Pseudemys scripta elegans*).

animal species or globule color. The absorption spectra closely resemble ideal bandpass filter spectra for the visible range, with a steep, smooth upward slope at the long wavelengths and a decrease in absorption below 400 mμ except for green and "colorless" globules. The absorption spectra of the colorless globules resemble more closely those of typical carotenoid spectra, matching that of galloxanthin, a retinal carotenoid identified from the chicken (Wald, 1948). The absorption peak of the "colorless" globule also corresponds closely to the single absorption maximum of all-trans retinene$_1$ in carbon disulfide at 398 mμ (Hubbard, Gregerman, and Wald, 1953).

These colored retinal oil globules have been postulated as the basis for the observed increase in spectral sensitivity of these animals to red light as compared to animals without them (Donner, 1950; Fox, 1953; Walls, 1942). The effect of colored globules on the spectral sensitivity of the pigeon retina has been discussed by Donner (1950, 1953), using electrophysiological data. He observed three "modulator" curves for the pigeon, with maxima at 470-490, 540-550, and 600-620 mμ. Comparison with three similar curves obtained

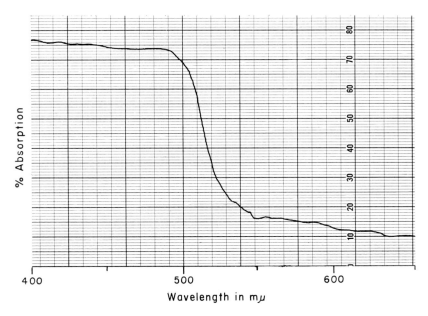

Figure 48 Absorption spectrum of the yellow colored oil globule in the frog retina.

by Granit (1941) for the frog retina revealed a shift to longer wavelengths for the pigeon. On the basis of the observed shift, Donner (1953) calculated what the absorption spectra of the oil globules in the pigeon should be. Figure 46 shows a comparison between Donner's calculated values (dotted lines) and the spectra Strother (1963) obtained (solid lines). The oil globules' absorption, then, could account for the red shift in the pigeon spectral sensitivity.

Spectral sensitivity for the swamp turtle, using electroretinogram techniques, shows maxima at 575, 620, and 645 mμ. Absorption spectra recorded in our laboratory, for their colored oil globules (Fig. 47) shows absorption maxima for the red globules from 555-565 mμ, for the yellow globules from 510-515 mμ, and for the "colorless" globules from 370-380 mμ. On the assumption that the spectral response of the turtle eye corresponds to the absorption curve of its cone pigment, cyanopsin, Strother (1963) has shown that one can obtain spectral absorption peaks at 625 and 650 mμ, which is in agreement with two of the spectral responses obtained from the electroretinograms.

It is of interest, then, to compare these absorption peaks to cyanopsin, curve shown in Figure 17. But, as already indicated, there are at least three and probably more absorption peaks for cone pigments in the living state, and therefore the cyanopsin curve is probably a smoothed-out approximation of the turtle cone pigments.

It is interesting to compare the cone data (also Fig. 42) with the chicken, pigeon, and turtle oil globules (Figs. 45, 46, 47) and with the yellow oil globules of the frog (Fig. 48). The frog also possesses "green" rods with an absorption maximum near 540 mμ and another peak near 610 mμ, and cones with an absorption maximum near 570 mμ. These absorption peaks, taken together, would cover the spectral range necessary for color vision.

Since these globules are located mainly between the inner and outer segments of the retinal cones, they are then in an excellent position to act as structures in the energy transfer. The theoretical feasibility of this role of the carotenoids has been discussed (Platt, 1959), but whether this function can also be assigned to the colored globules remains to be investigated. Finally, quantitative evaluation of the filtering effect of colored oil globules must await more detailed data on *in vivo* absorption of cone pigments.

TISSUE CULTURE OF RETINAL CELLS

Human, embryonic (four to five months) retinal ganglion cells and rabbit, chicken, and frog retinal cells, as well as nerve and brain cells from new-born rats and kittens, and cells from the visual cortex have been tissue cultured and studied (Geiger, 1958; Liss and Wolter, 1961; Vinnikov, 1946; Yoshida, 1960).

The retinas from the eyes of freshly killed frogs, chickens, and cattle were used in our studies, but only the cattle retina will be illustrated to show how tissue culture methods can be applied to the study of retinal cells (Wolken and Ward, 1962).

The cattle retinas were minced and placed in a petri dish containing Medium 199 and 20 per cent calf serum, and then incubated in the dark at 37°C. The chemical composition of the synthetic Medium 199 is that described by Morgan, Morten, and Parker (1950) and modified by Younger, Ward, and Salk (1952). To each 100 ml. of Medium—199, 3 ml. of a 2.8 per cent sodium bicar-

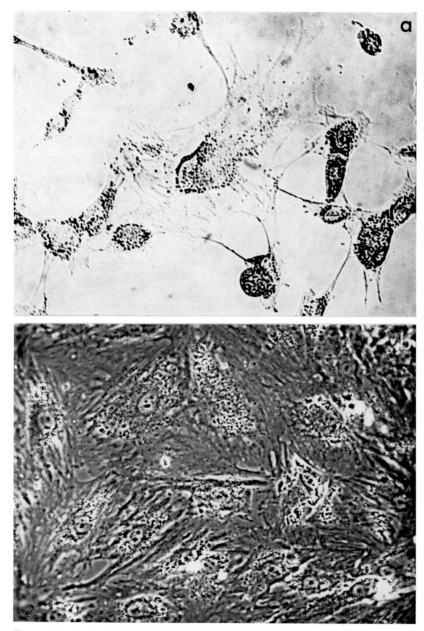

Figure 49a Living bovine retinal cells of a 2 day old tissue culture. X 240.
b. Living bovine retinal cells of a 2 day old tissue culture, phase contrast. X 260.

bonate solution was added. In addition to calf serum (inactivated at 56°C for one-half hour), the following antibiotics were used: dihydro-streptomycin sulfate, 200 μg per ml.; neomycin, 100 μg per ml.; penicillin G, 400 units per ml. The pH of the medium is initially 7.2 to 7.4. It rises to pH 8.0 upon incubation, and during the course of growth falls to pH 6.8 due to cell metabolism.

The glass surfaces of culture bottles, petri dishes, cover glasses, and plastic films provided the substrate for these monolayer cultures. The nutrient medium was changed at ten, twelve, and fourteen days, and on the eighteenth day the cells were trypsinized and a new cell culture made (subculture 1). Three days later, a solid sheet of clear stellate cells was present, and these were again trypsinized and an additional cell culture made (subculture 2). In another three days, the bottle surface was completely covered with elongated, contiguous cells, many of which were in division.

These cattle retinal cells have been continuously subcultured as

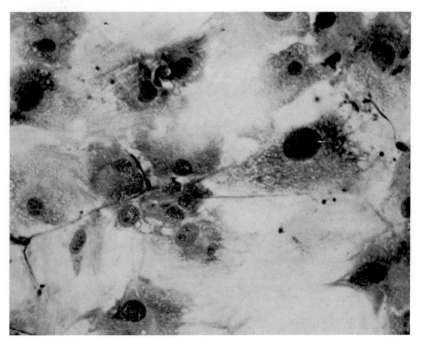

Figure 50 Tissue culture of retinal cells fixed in 95% alcohol and stained with methylene blue (a 15 day culture). X 290

described, with the time of subculturing varying from seven to fourteen to twenty-one days. Although the growth rate is slow, it is significant that the cell population doubles every 10 to 14 days. For example, from an inoculum of 0.025 ml. (1.5×10^6 cells) in 60 ml. of medium, after fourteen days' incubation, 2.5×10^6 cells were collected.

An interesting observation in these cultures was that not all the retinal rods degenerate, and in a few cultures they were maintained for as long as twenty-eight days. Also, when cultures are maintained in the same vessel for long periods of time (six months or more), the cells show no degenerative changes and continue to grow until two or more cell layers formed.

Depending on the age of the culture, considerable variation in cell size and shape is observed. In a continuous cell line, there are

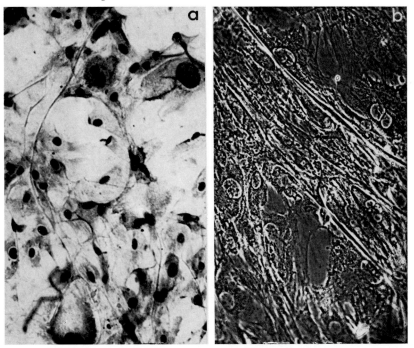

Figure 51a Tissue cultured (98 day culture) retinal cells fixed with Carnoy and gallocyanin stain. Note the long interconnecting fibers. X 195
   b. Living tissue cultured (98 day) cells. Note the highly refractile fibers. Phase contrast. X 175

three distinct cell sizes: large ($<100\mu$); medium (<30 to 60μ), which predominate; and small (<10 to 20μ). The nuclei in these cells are oval or round and contain from 2 to 9 nucleoli. Many fat droplets surround the nuclei, and the cytoplasm is extensive and full of small granules (Figs. 49 and 50).

When cultivated in the same vessel, at the end of the second week and always in the third week, small, bulbous bodies appear in the cytoplasm of these cells. From these bodies, fiber-like processes appear, which eventually interlace the whole culture (Figs. 50, 51a, and 52). In very old preparations, there is a network of these fibers which seems to originate in areas where the cells are close together. The fibers then grow out and surround either single cells or small groups of cells (Fig. 51). The older the culture, the thicker this fibrous material becomes, and random swellings develop along the fibers (Fig. 51).

Some nerve cells and nerve fibers have an affinity for methylene

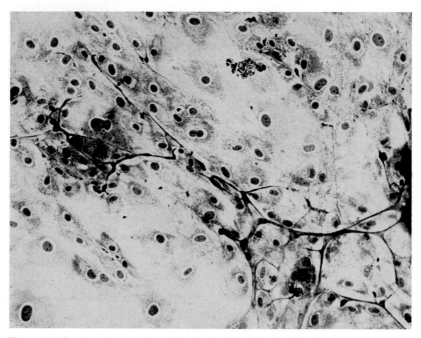

Figure 52 Bovine tissue cultured cells fixed and stained with gallocyanin and yellow napthol. X 290

blue, and in 95 per cent alcohol and methylene blue the cytoplasmic material and the fibers are stained blue (Figs. 50 and 53). Osmium tetroxide (OsO₄), a fixative for lipids, stains the cytoplasmic material black and the fibers gray to black (Fig. 54a). Using formalin and Bodian's silver stain, the cytoplasmic material stains black, and dots of silver outline the fibers (Fig. 54b). With formalin and Mallory's phosphotungstic acid hematoxylin, the cytoplasmic material is unstained, but in some places along the fibers there is a faint purple color. The cytoplasmic material and the fibers are unstained with formalin fixation and Sudan black B. Histochemical reactions indicate that the fibers are mostly protein.

The ganglion layer of the retina contains glia cells that act as connective and supporting tissues. Among the different types of glia cells are the fibers of Müller, Golgi's spider cells, astrocytes, and microglia. (Glees, 1955). The fibers of Müller are long, narrow, complicated structures that pass through the whole thickness of the retina from the internal to the external limiting membranes. Golgi's

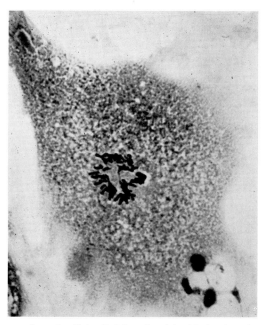

Figure 53 Tissue cultured cell in division, fixed in 95% ethanol, methylene blue stain. X 705

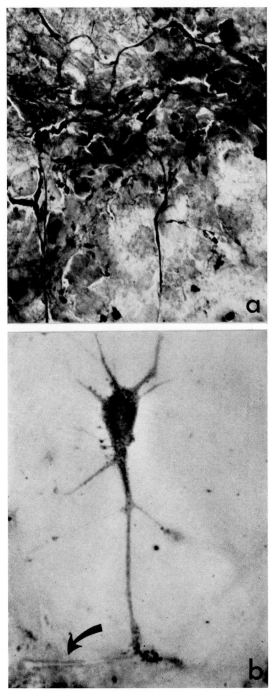

Figure 54a Tissue cultured cells, fixed in 1% OsO₄ showing the fibrillar
network. X 170.
b. A cell from a 28 day culture fixed in 10% formalin and stained with
Bodian silver stain. X 1590

spider cells are small glial cells with a round or oval nucleus and numerous cytoplasmic processes. Astrocytes, or star cells, are found at random throughout the ganglion cell layer (pigment granules are also to be found). Microglia are phagocytic, wandering cells, that are round, oval, or rod-shaped. It is difficult to compare these cultured cells with histological sections of the intact retinal nervous cell layers, They do, however, resemble those of the central nervous system and are similar to those illustrated in Liss and Wolter (1961), Geiger (1957, 1958), and Last (1961).

An important question is whether these tissue cultured cells structurally fulfill the electrophysiological requirements; to do so, they should respond to light. Rushton (1953) indicates that they should be large cell bodies of the order of 30 to 50μ, with branches that spread in all directions in a circle of at least 1 mm. The large cells and the more numerous medium cells that we observe fulfill the size requirement and could well behave like the neurons with their dendritic processes. The smaller cells are probably a mixture of glia type cells. It has been suggested that such neuroglia cells transfer energy rich compounds, ATP (adenosine triphosphate), to the nerve cells (Heyden, 1960). Electron microscopic studies indicate a morphologic association of neuroglia and neurons in the toad retina (Lassansky, 1961). Electron micrographs of these cells show neural-like structures (see Figs. 55 and 56) and many myelin figures (Fig. 57). It is not surprising, therefore, that these two types of collaborating cells grow simultaneously in our cultures. The examination of these different histological cell types of the nervous system in respect to cell behavior becomes, then, an increasingly important study (Willmer, 1960).

Electrophysiology—To discover whether these cells react to light,

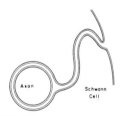

Figure 55 Diagram of a Schwann cell.

electrophysiological techniques were applied. Microelectrodes (micro-probes) with tips of the order of 0.5μ filled with 3 MKCl were used. The apparatus assembled for electrophysiological measurements in-

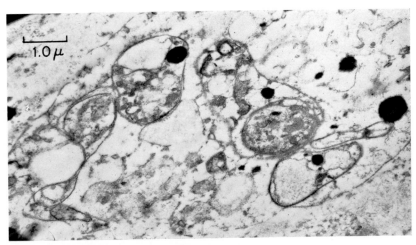

Figure 56 Bovine tissue cultured cells, showing neural-like structures.

Figure 57 Myelin structures found in the tissue cultured cells.

cludes a micromanipulator, monochromator, electrical stimulator, special amplifiers, and a recorder, is shown in Figure 58.

Neurons in tissue culture differ from those *in vivo* in one important aspect. A neuron *in vivo* is always part of a neural network, whereas a neuron in tissue culture no longer has synaptic connections with other neurons. Therefore, it is only under these experimental conditions that we can investigate the properties of central neurons without being confused by the effects of nerve impulses at the synapses.

Neurons of the central nervous system, in response to intracellular stimulation, give rise to action potentials which resemble the responses obtained from neurons *in vivo* by previous investigations (Hild and Tasaki, 1962). Some experimental studies indicate that nerve impulses can invade the dendrites.

It was found that the input impedance (grid current), the noise level, and the input capacitance are important for measuring the membrane and the action potentials. The recording device must be fast, the grid current very low (less than 10^{-12}Amp). The cells

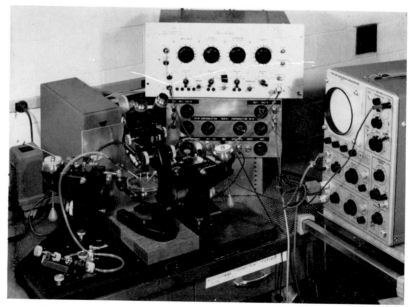

Figure 58 Instrumentation for electrophysiological measurements.

are very easily damaged by transverse movements as the electrode enters the cell, but microelectrodes with tip diameters of 0.5μ could be inserted into the cell without impaling it. The use of phase microscopy was necessary to discriminate between cells.

The aim of our investigations was to find out if cells grown in single layers in tissue culture had formed any synaptic connections. The membrane potentials of the cells varied between 10 mV. and 35 mV. (Fig. 59). The magnitude of this potential did not appear to be related to the type or the size of the cells. It was not expected that all cell types would be excitable, and Hild and Tasaki (1962) point out that the metabolic condition of the cells is very important.

Light and electrical stimulation were used to elicit cell responses; no light responses were obtained, but the cells could be stimulated electrically. Using inside stimulation via the measuring electrode and outside stimulation with the help of an extra electrode, cell responses could not be recorded with stimuli comparable to those used by Hild and Tasaki (1962). Sporadic reactions, however, were observed which could be recorded. The finding that some neurons in tissue culture are firing impulses spontaneously is not surprising; it is known that isolated skeletal fibers in tissue culture twitch spontaneously.

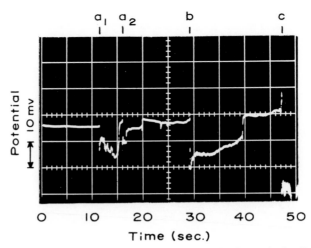

Figure 59 Membrane potential of a tissue cultured bovine retinal cell as photograph of a record from the oscilloscope.

These experimental studies, still in the beginnings, do offer promising possibilities for looking more closely at cells from the nerve layers of the retina in tissue culture.

Chapter VI

INVERTEBRATE PHOTORECEPTORS

STRUCTURE

The invertebrates, which include protozoa, coelenterates, flat-worms, arthropods, and molluscs, possess such diverse eye structures as light-sensitive eyespots and sensory cells and ocelli and image-forming compound eyes. There seems, however, to be no common denominator between the development of vertebrate eyes and the differentiation of the eyes of the invertebrates. All vertebrate eyes are homologous organs of the same embryonic origin; their diversity is exclusively a matter of organization. Invertebrate eyes are not homologous; their origins differ, even from one family to another.

While the structure and pigment chemistry of the invertebrate eyes have not been studied as thoroughly as the vertebrate eye, it is known that in some respects the mechanisms of vision are strikingly similar and are therefore of considerable interest.

To see whether there is some basic scheme for photoreception, a phylogenetic survey of the invertebrate eye structures and their pigments was carried out, from the eyespots of protozoa to the compound eyes of arthropods and molluscs (Wolken, 1957, 1958a, b, 1960a, 1961a, b, 1963). It was hoped that through such a comparative analysis, the invertebrate eyes would give us some clues to the vertebrate eye and vision.

The protozoan algal flagellate, *Euglena*, possesses a simple receptor-effector system, an eyespot for light capture and a flagellum (Fig. 60). The eyespot (stigma in *Euglena* is an agglomeration of 40 to 50 dense, pigmented orange to red granules varying in size from 0.1 to 0.3μ in diameter, which forms a cross-section of $2 \times 3\mu$. The granules of the eyespot are located immediately below the membrane of the reservoir, a smooth-walled chamber that follows the ridged gullet in which the initial part of the flagellum is found (Fig 60 a, b, c, and d). A system of regularly spaced fibrillae is found between the granules and the membrane of the reservoir (Fig. 60b). A dense, homogeneous body attached to the flagellum and facing the eyespot is identified as the paraflagellar body or its photoreceptor (Wolken and Palade, 1953; Wolken, 1956b, 1961c).

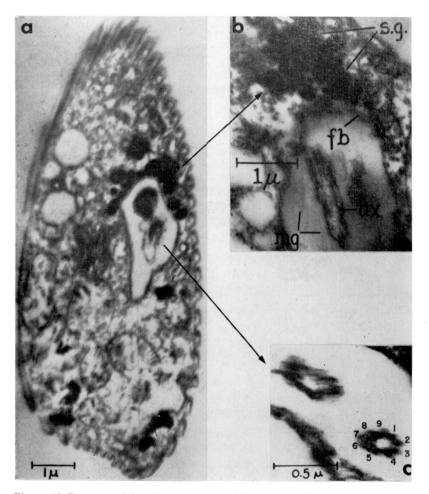

Figure 60 Eyespot and flagellum structures of *Euglena gracilis*.
    a. Cross-section of whole organism, showing eyespot granules (s.g.) surrounding gullet and base of flagellum.
    b. Showing mastigonemeta (mg) of the flagella; the fibrillar (fb) system of the reservoir; and the axonemata (ax).
    c. Fibrils of the flagellum.

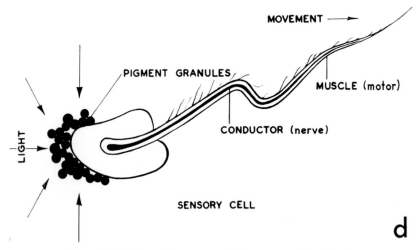

Figure 60d. Schematic sensory cell (eyespot and flagellum).

Euglena responds to a light stimulus by swimming towards it or away from it depending upon its intensity and wavelength. Similarities between phototaxis in these organisms and the visual process in animals has been suggested; therefore, *Euglena* is an ideal organism for this kind of study (Wolken, 1961c).

Photokinesis, the rate of swimming without directed orientation, is dependent upon the absolute amount of light energy absorbed. The rate of motion is constant for a constant light intensity, changing as the intensity is varied, but it takes ten to fifteen minutes for a change in velocity to take place following a change in the intensity of illumination. The rate of swimming in white light at two foot-candles rises sharply from 0.11 mm/sec. to the maximum rate of 0.16 mm/sec. at forty foot-candles (Fig. 61a) its saturation intensity (Wolken and Shin, 1958).

The action spectrum for the rate of swimming (mean velocity in mm/sec versus wavelength at four foot-candles of light intensity) is illustrated in Figure 62, which shows a major peak at 465 mμ and another at 630 mμ. The spectral sensitivity curve for phototaxis shows a major peak at 490 mμ with some response near 420 mμ and beyond 600 mμ (Fig. 63a). This spectrum for phototaxis is compared to that of photokinesis in Figure 63b.

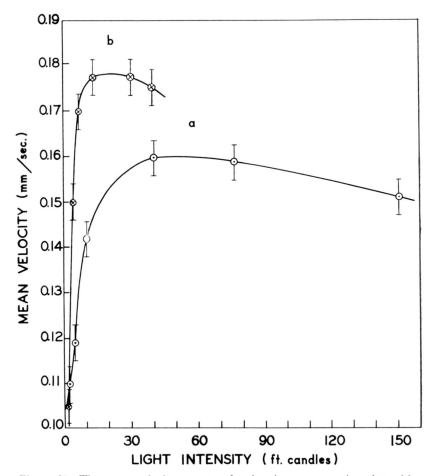

Figure 61a The mean velocity or rate of swimming versus various intensities. (a) white light, (b) polarized light. *Euglena gracilis.*

The problem of motility, although complex in itself, involves the more general problems of reception, excitation, contractility, and, possibly, neural transmission. If there is a connection between the absorbed light and the motility of cells, as has been suggested by these behavioral experiments, there must exist some mechanism for transmission of information from the receptor (eyespot) to the effector (flagellum).

The fact that by means of the intensity and wavelength of light

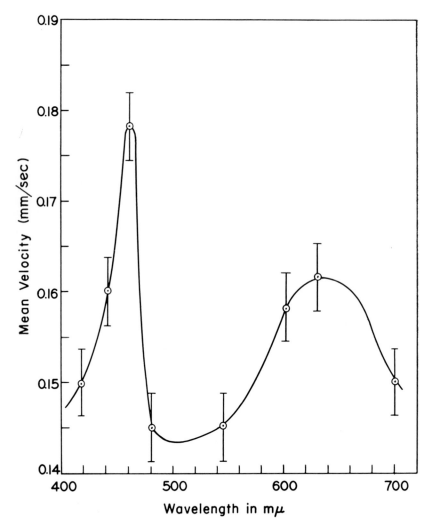

Figure 62 Photokinesis action spectra for the rate of swimming (measured at
4 foot-candles). *Euglena gracilis.*

we can communicate with the organism to the extent that its speed
and direction of motion are controlled, suggests a sensory cell, or
its analog, a photocell. The eyespot + flagellum may therefore be
regarded as a servo- or feedback-mechanism, which maintains an
optimal level of illumination in the organism, and has some analogies
to a primitive form of nervous system.

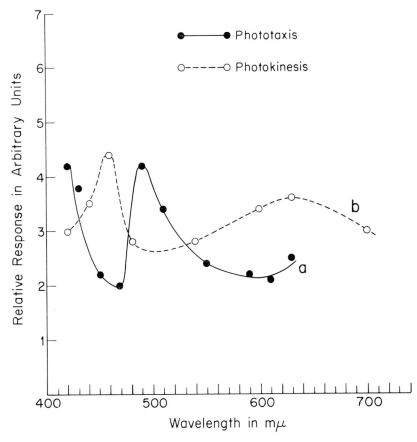

Figure 63 Phototaxis and photokinesis. (swimming reactions). *Euglena gracilis.*
  a. Phototaxis.
  b. Photokinesis.

The chemistry of the flagellum indicates that it is composed almost entirely of protein similar perhaps to myosin, the contractile protein in muscle. The movement of flagella and the contraction of muscle appear to be kindred processes, since the mechanism may be controlled by a similar molecule, adenosine triphosphate (ATP). Also, experimental analysis indicates that in each *Euglena* cell there are about 3.85×10^2 molecules of acetylcholine, a chemical compound associated with the chemistry of nerve cell function.

The flagellum consists of nine elementary fibrils or filaments (axonemata) embedded in a matrix and covered by a common membrane, similar to that of a nerve axon. Two additional fibrils may be paired in the center of the flagellum. This general pattern of organization is found for flagella and cilia in all plant and animal cells (observe as in Figure 33a, where a similar flagellum connects the inner and outer segments of the vertebrate rods). The base of the flagellum is situated in a vacuole very close to the eyespot as illustrated in Figure 60a, b, d, but it is not known how the flagellum is attached to the eyespot.

That the energy flow from receptor to effector is not continuous, but is in unit pulses, could be due to a certain threshold phenomenon associated with the photo-and electro-chemistry at the base of the flagellum near or at the eyespot. These are observed as successive trial and error movements in the course of searching for the place of optimum illumination.

If we consider that the information received at the eyespot in terms of light quanta of various frequencies and intensities is converted into some other form of signal and that this new signal is transmitted to the flagellum in such a way that the resulting responses are consistant with the initial information received at the eyespot, we can conceive of the following simple mechanism that will explain the transmission of information from the eyespot to the flagellum. The information may be transmitted by means of pulses of a constant height, where time of duration between two pulses defines the information being transmitted. Each pulse carries a certain constant amount of energy, so that the net amount of energy transmitted to the flagellum per unit time is directly proportional to the number of pulses carried per unit time. A change in wavelength of the light incident on the eyespot brings a change in the time interval between two pulses (the time interval decreases as the spectral effectiveness increases); a change in light intensity also brings a change in the time of duration between two pulses. The "steering mechanism" that selects the direction of movement is good only for selection between two directions, movement towards and movement away from light.

From the area of the photoreceptor, the effective wavelength, and the light intensity, the energy necessary to produce a response can be roughly calculated. Our estimation of the energy threshold for *Euglena* is 1.7×10^{-11} ergs, or a quantum efficiency of 14 per cent. At this frequency, the number of photons that can excite the "eye" is seven. It is interesting to note that the human eye can detect a minimum of four photons at around 500 mμ.

The shape of the velocity versus intensity curve in Figure 61 showing a gradual rise, with increase in the intensity and the appearance of plateaus at higher intensity values, is very similar to the current-intensity curve of a photoconductive cell.

It has been suggested that the creation of nerve impulses in visual processes may be considered as an event in which some electrical-chemical energy is released by means of reactions derived from photoactivation of rhodopsin (Rosenberg, 1958). While in the photo-receptors of higher animals the photoexcitation triggers electrical events in the receptors, the greater part of the energy contained in a receptor discharge is derived from chemical energy. Thus, the number of electronic charges involved in forming one such discharge is much larger than the minimum number of light quanta required to trigger the discharge. In the case of *Euglena,* however, such an amplification mechanism is not necessary. The minimum number of quanta required to excite the eyespot is comparable to the power involved in the swimming motion. This means that one light quantum which is effectively absorbed at the eyespot can be associated with approximately one electronic charge delivered to the base of the flagellum. At the saturation intensity of about 40 foot-candles, the swimming velocity is about 0.013 mm/sec in a medium of viscosity 0.987 centipoises. Using the cross-section of the eyespot, the intensity of 40 foot-candles at wavelength 465 mμ (equivalent to about 2×10^{14} quanta per cm^2 per sec), and the average radius of the *Euglena,* we have estimated the threshold potential to be of the order of 0.01-0.1 millivolts. This is considered small in comparison with the values found for nerve cells of vertebrates.

The question of whether a characteristic threshold potential really exists and whether the energy transfer is done electrically may be answered by measuring the potential drop between the eyespot and the flagellum, but such measurements are difficult to make. Preliminary experimental results using microelectrode and electrophysi-

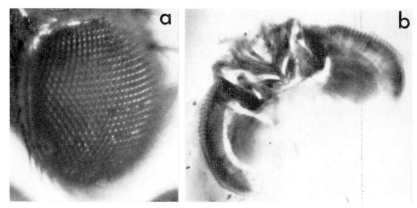

Figure 64 *Drosophila melanogaster.*
a. Photograph of the living eye. X 125
b. A section of the whole eye; x-ray micrograph. X 80

ological recording techniques, indicate that dark$<$---$>$light electrical changes do occur. These are <0.10 mv on light stimulation.
Such weak responses were also found in the retinal receptors of an
insect (Naka, 1960).

As we approach higher levels of development, the flatworms *(Platyhelminthes)*, the common Planarian for example, possess two eyes,
ocelli, consisting of pigment granules and sensory cells that continue
from the eye as nerves entering the brain. The pigment granules
shade the sensory cells from light in all but one direction, and so
enable the animal to respond differentially to the direction of light;
to turn from the light to the dark. The animal's tendency to avoid
light seems to be controlled by the balance of the impulses from the
eyes. The sensory cells have differentiated structures that resemble
retinal cells and which probably function analogously to the retinal
rods of the vertebrate eye. They are about 5μ in diameter, with
an average length of approximately 35μ, and they consist of tightly
packed tubules of the order of 400-500 Å in diameter (Wolken,
1958a, 1961b). Similar sensory cell structures have also been found
in the planarians, *Dugesia lugubris* and *Dendrocoelum lacteum* (Rölich and Török, 1961) and in the marine planarian *Convoluta ros-
coffensis* (peculiar to the Coast of Brittany, France).

The arthropods, which comprise the major part of the invertebrates,
include insects, arachnids, and crustaceans, and all possess image-

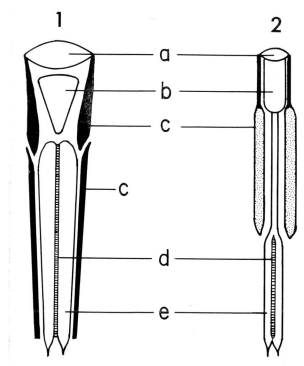

Figure 65 Schematic diagram of the two types of ommatidia in the insect compound eye. 1. *Apposition* eye. 2. *Superposition* eye. a. cornea (lens); b. crystalline cone; c. pigment sheath; d. rhabdome; e. retinula cells.

forming compound eyes. The compound eye consists of ommatidia (eye facets) that vary in number from only a few, as in some species of ants, to more than 2,000 in the dragonfly. (Note the compound eye of *Drosophila* at low magnification in Fig. 64 and 66a).

Each ommatidium (Figs. 65 and 67) has a cornea (a lens), crystalline cone, and, depending on the organism, from three to more than eleven retinal cells. The retinal cells form "light-trapping" rhabdomes (the retina) where the visual process is initiated. The rhabdomeres (photoreceptors) are differentiated, specialized, centralized processes of the retinal cells, and are considered analogous in function to the retinal rods of the vertebrate eye.

Let us examine, then, the compound eye structure of a few insects. The eye of the fruitfly, *Drosophila melanogaster*, for example, is composed of over 700 ommatidia. The ommatidium consists of a corneal

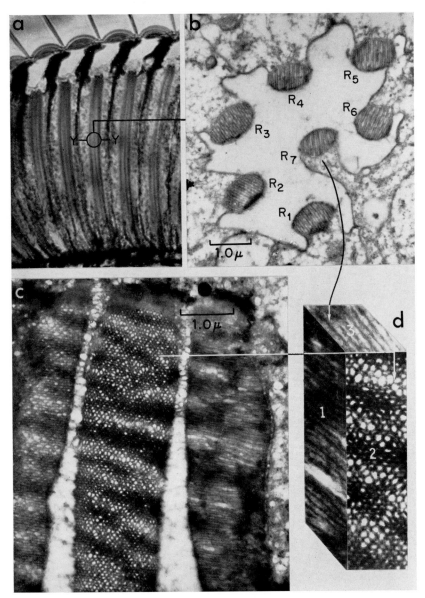

Figure 66 Eye structure, *Drosophila melanogaster*.

    a. Light micrograph of a longitudinal section through several ommatidia showing the cornea (lens), crystalline cone, rhabdome, and pigment sheath. (Refer also to diagram of an ommatidium, Fig. 67).

    b. Cross-section (Y-Y) through the rhabdome to illustrate the orientation of the rhabdomeres (photoreceptors) and their *fine structure*.

    c. Longitudinal section at the distal end of the ommatidium showing three adjacent rhabdomeres and their *fine structure*.

    d. A reconstructed section through a rhabdomere to indicate a three-dimensional structure (surfaces 1,2,3, as in Fig. 67d).

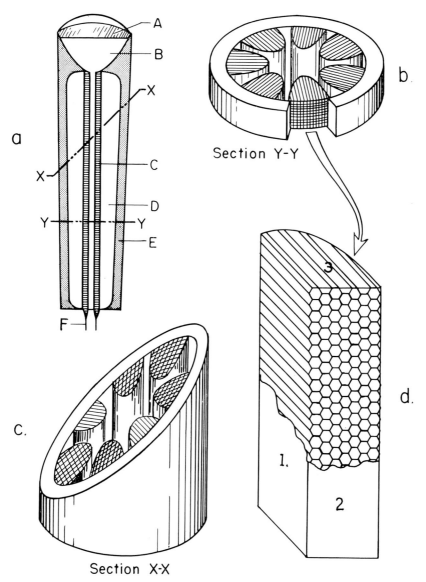

Figure 67 Diagram of an insect ommatidium. (also refer to Fig. 65).

a. Longitudinal section of a complete ommatidium (A) cornea (lens); (B) crystalline cone; (C) rhabdomere; (D) retinula cell; (E) pigment sheath; (F) nerve fiber from the retinal cell. Cross-section Y-Y; oblique section X-X.

b. Three-dimensional cross-section (Y-Y) through the ommatidium showing the lamellar pattern in all of the radially arranged rhabdomeres.

c. Three-dimensional oblique section (X-X) through the ommatidium.

d. Three-dimensional section of a rhabdomere. Two sides are cut away revealing (1 and 3) a lamellar structure and (2) a hexagonal (tubular) structure.

lens, a crystalline cone, seven retinula cells and their rhabdomeres, and a sheath of pigment cells that extends over its entire length (Wolken, 1957; Wolken *et al.,* 1957a, b). The pigment sheath is not found in the white-eyed mutants. Each ommatidium is about 17μ in diameter and from $70\text{-}125\mu$ in length (Fig. 66a).

In cross-section (Fig. 66b), the seven retinula cells are radially arranged, each having a medial portion extending toward the center of the ommatidium and terminating in a dense, circular rhabdomere. The rhabdomeres are situated in a relatively clear fluid cavity. Each rhabdomere is distinct with respect to the retinula cells, with a finely differentiated line of attachment between them. Electron micrographs show that the rhabdome is made of seven individual rhabdomeres, $R_1 — R_7$, each averaging 1.2μ in diameter and 60μ in length. A definite *fine structure* is observable within each of the rhabdomeres, which consist of parallel dense bands (lamellae) about 100 Å in thickness, separated by less dense interspaces. These dense laminations originate at the line of attachment and terminate in a scalloped border on the medial side of the rhabdomere, indicating that the lamellar structure probably represents tubules (double-membranes) that are closely packed and extend away from the retinula cell toward the center of the ommatidium.

The lamellar pattern is found in all cross-sections of the rhabdomeres, while a tubular pattern is seen in some oblique and longitudinal sections. Rhabdomeres which show the tubular structure have no differentiated line of attachment to the retinula cell. A combination of the tubular and lamellar structures is illustrated in Fig. 66b and c.

A single structure which produces two different geometrical patterns in thin section, depends entirely upon the orientation of the individual rhabdomere with respect to the plane of cutting. Each rhabdomere appears to consist of double-membraned tubes of about 500 Å in diameter, with walls of the order of 50 Å in thickness.

A three-dimensional section of a rhabdomere was constructed from the electron micrographs (Fig 66d, 67d) by fitting three surfaces together to illustrate a single structural unit of packed tubes (Wolken *et al.,* 1957a).

Another example is the cockroach, since it is one of the more primitive of the unspecialized insects. Electrophysiological studies have suggested that cockroach eyes contain two types of visual re-

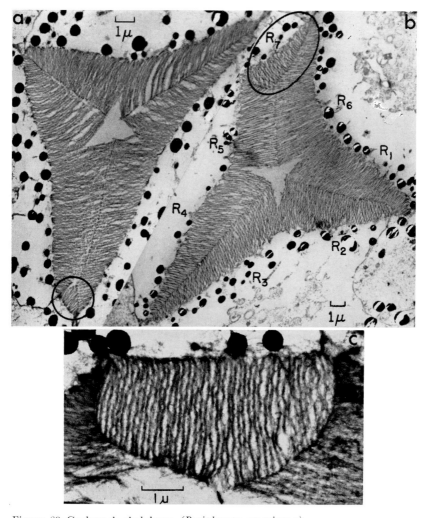

Figure 68 Cockroach rhabdome *(Periplaneta americana).*

a and b. Cross-section through two rhabdomeres showing the arrangement of the seven rhabdomeres (R_1 to R_7) which form each rhabdome. Note the assymetrical rhabdomere (circled) and the *fine structure* of the rhabdomeres.

 c. A cross-section of an asymmetrical rhabdomere showing the lamellae.

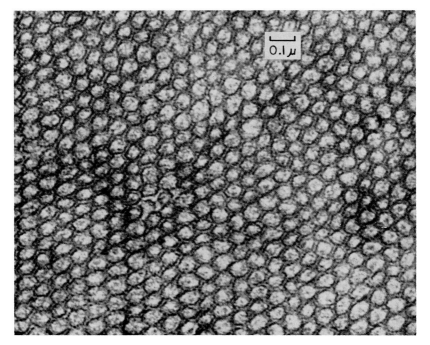

Figure 69 *Fine structure* of the photoreceptor of *Daphnia pulex;* note packing
of tubules.

ceptor systems (Walther and Dodt, 1957, 1959; Walther, 1958).
The compound eyes of two common, large species of cockroaches
investigated, *Periplaneta americana* and *Blaberus giganteus,* are composed of approximately 2,000 ommatidia. The ommatidia are separated from one another by a pigment sheath extending to the
basement membrane of the eye (to the nerves and tracheae). The
structure of their photoreceptors is therefore of interest for comparison to those of other insects.

A cross-section through the cockroach eye shows many ommatidia
surrounded by pigment granules (Fig. 68). Each ommatidium appears to be made up of seven retinula cells. The retinula cell is
from 7 to 9μ in diameter with a large elliptical nucleus, and the
inner side is differentiated to form the rhabdomere. The rhabdomere
averages 2μ in diameter and is about 100μ in length. All seven
rhabdomeres are in close proximity and form the rhabdome. Ag-

gregates of intracellular pigment granules, which do not seem to be affected by dark-adaptation, surround the rhabdomes and extend the whole length of the retinula cells. Numerous mitochondria are dispersed throughout the retinula cell. Depending upon the location and angle of cut, the rhabdome can appear either as a rhomboid or as a triangle (with sides measuring from 5 to 12μ in length). Each rhabdome is made up of seven rhabdomeres which exhibit a regular pattern of organization; one of the rhabdomeres is asymmetrical (R_7 Fig. 68a, b, c); the others are arranged in pairs. In all rhabdomes, the main axes of the paired rhabdomeres have the same orientation with respect to the asymmetrical rhabdomere.

The cockroach rhabdomeres are also a single geometrical structure of tightly packed tubules (Fig. 68). Each tubule is about 500 Å in diameter with walls of the order of 50 Å in thickness. There are approximately 400 tubules in $1\mu^2$ of surface, or about 80,000 tubules in a single rhabdomere (Wolken and Gupta, 1961).

The number of retinula cells in the upper and lower halves of the cockroach compound eyes does not differ, but there are minor variations in the relative size of the retinula cells. No histological differences were found between the upper and lower halves of the compound eye of the cockroaches, which is in agreement with previous studies of Walther (1958). We have observed that there are seven retinula cells which form the rhabdome, although eight such visual cells were found in the cochroaches *Blatta (Stylopyga) orientalis* and *Blatella germanica* (Jörschke, 1914; Nowikoff, 1932). This eighth cell is probably a rudimentary structure located close to the basal membrane (Dietrich, 1909). It does not extend the entire length of the rhabdome, and no rhabdomere is differentiated from it.

The crustacea are many and varied, but we have examined the compound eye structures of two closely related fresh-water species, *Leptodora kindtii* and *Daphnia magna,* and a marine copepod, *Copilia quadrata* (Figs. 69-73).

Leptodora kindtii, a carnivorous zooplankton, is common to many fresh-water lakes and ponds in North America, Europe, and Asia. It is believed to have vision superior to all others in its class, for it pursues and captures copepods as large and as fast as a *Cyclops* for food.

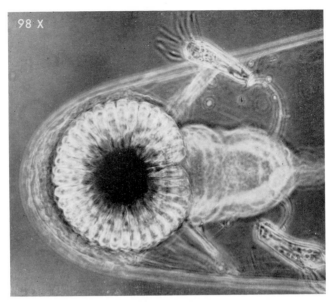

Figure 70 *Leptodora kindtii.* Living eye. X 98.

Leptodora possesses one median eye, composed of approximately 500 ommatidia radially arranged 360° (Fig. 70). The ommatidia are large, conical structures, 180μ in length and from 30μ in diameter at the outer portion to just a few microns at the base. A cross-section of the eye is shown in Fig. 71. The crystalline cone constitutes about two-thirds of the ommatidial length. Although it is rounded at the outer end, there is no evidence of a distinguishable lens cap. There is interstitial space which is completely transparent and probably functions as a common lens for all ommatidia between the surface of the eye sphere and the external chitinous wall. The crystalline cone is composed of five, equal pie-shaped segments, which are formed from five crystalline cone cells (Fig. 72a, b). The crystalline cone serves to concentrate the light into a narrow beam. Whether or not the segmentation promotes a system of total internal reflection is not known. Although structural data shows that the crystalline cone continues proximally to the surface of the rhabdome as in the apposition type eye, observations of pigment migration indicate that under certain conditions of dark-adaptation, "crossing" among adjacent crystalline cones could result in the formation of a superposition image. As the cones con-

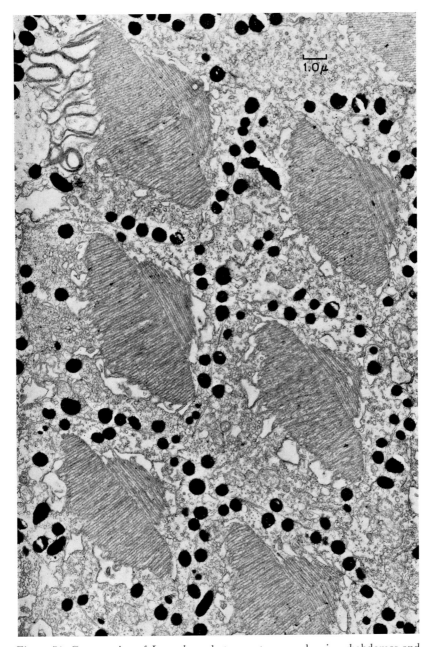

Figure 71 Cross-section of *Leptodora* photoreceptor area showing rhabdomes and its fused rhabdomeres.

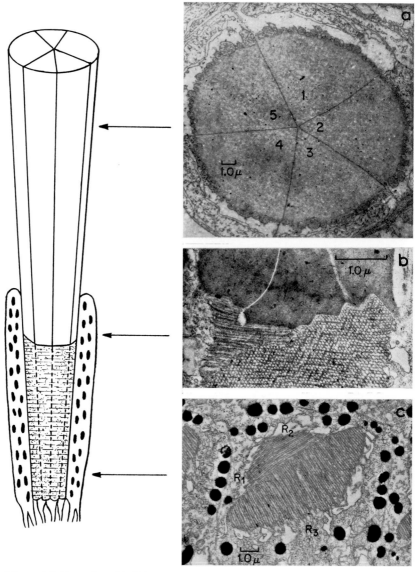

Figure 72 *Leptodora kindtii:* ommatidium.
    a. Crystalline cone.
    b. Connection of crystalline cone with the rhabdomere.
    c. A fused rhabdome, photoreceptors R_1 R_2, R_3, its rhabdomeres.

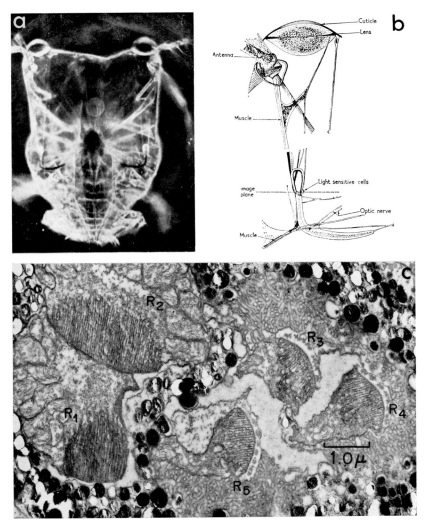

Figure 73 *Copilia quadrata*
    a. Light micrograph (Courtesy of Dr. Neville Moray, University of Sheffield, Sheffield, England). X 45
    b. Schematic of eye (modified from Grenacher, 1879).
    c. Cross-section, of a single ommatidium with an open type rhabdome and its 5 rhabdomeres, the photoreceptors.

tinue inward, the space between them increases and is filled with pigment cells.

The rhabdomes are directly affixed to the ends of the crystalline cones (Fig. 72b). *Leptodora* has four retinula cells that give rise to a closed rhabdome composed of three fused rhabdomeres (Fig. 72c). The rhabdomeres are tubular structures as observed in all the arthropod eyes examined. One of the rhabdomeres is larger than the combined size of the other two and is formed by two of the four retinula cells. The microvilli (tubules) of the small rhabdomes are perpendicular to those of the large rhabdomes. The average diameter of the rhabdome is about 4μ with tubules measuring 500 Å in diameter. The ends of the microvilli appear to be open and continuous with the cytoplasm of the retinula cells. The outside diameter of the tubules is about 500 Å; the inside diameter is about 400 Å and the thickness of the wall is from 50-100 Å. The general structure of the four retinula cells that give rise to three fused rhabdomeres (Fig. 72c) is very similar to *Anisoptera*, the dragonfly (Naka, 1960).

The marine copepod, *Copilia quadrata,* is found in the plankton layer at a depth of 150 to 200 meters in the Bay of Naples (Fig. 73a). Only the female of the species possesses eyes (ocelli), and these occupy almost one-half the body (Gregory *et al.*, 1964). The photoreceptor cells are attached to a thin strand of muscle that appears to move the receptor rapidly back and forth in the focal plane of the lens, scanning the image in much the same way as the tube of a television camera (see schematic drawing of the eye structure in Fig. 73b). In cross-section, there are approximately seven retinula cells, but only five rhabdomeres can be distinguished (Fig. 73c). The organization of the rhabdome is that of the open type and is similar to that described for the fruitfly *(Drosophila),* the housefly, and other insects.

The eyes of the cephalopod molluscs, for example, the *Octopus,* have only a single lens, which in general physical organization resembles the vertebrate eye. The lens, however, is formed out of two halves joined together; the retina is not inverted as in the vertebrate eyes, and the photoreceptors are directly exposed to the incident light (Hess, 1943; Ramsey, 1952). Histological studies in-

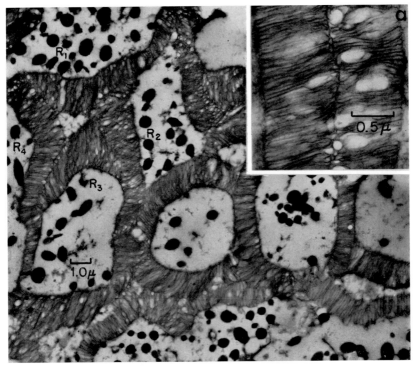

Figure 74 Cuttlefish, *Sepia officinalis*. An oblique section to show general geometry of rhabdome and *fine structure* of rhabdomeres.
a. Two fused rhabdomeres, showing lamellar structure.

dicate that the retina is made up of rhabdomes analogous to those of the arthropod compound eyes (Grenacher, 1886; Patten, 1887). J.Z. Young (1960, 1962) and his collaborators have used the *Octopus* as a model for their studies of visual acuity, eye-brain relationships, and learning processes. Because of these interests and the phylogenetic position of the *Octopus* in the scheme of visual development, it was desirable to obtain additional structural information on the retinal cells of the *Octopus*.

Octopus vulgaris and *Sepia officinalis* (cuttlefish) were obtained from the Bay of Naples and their eye structures studied with the electron microscope (Wolken, 1958b). Grenacher (1886) recognized a long time ago that the retina consists of rhabdomes, which he suggested are composed of four retinal cells. Thin sections of fixed

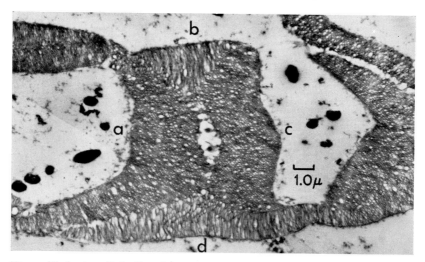

Figure 75 *Sepia officinalis.* Oblique section of rhabdome area, showing two rhabdomeres sides (a,c) tubular structure and two rhabdomeres (b,d) lamellar structure.

Octopus and *Sepia* retinas do show that the rhabdome consists of four radially arranged rhabdomeres (Figs. 74 and 75). The term rhabdomeres, as used here, follows the terminology used for the visual photoreceptors of the insect ommatidia, but they are more analogous to the vertebrate retinal rods.

In a cross-section through the rhabdomes, four sides of the rhabdomeres are isolated by pigment cells containing screening pigment granules that migrate depending on the light intensity. The rhabdomeres are from 50 to 60μ in length and from 1.0 to 1.5μ in diameter. Depending on the angle of cutting, the rhabdomeres appear as plates or packed tubes. In all cross-sections, the lamellar structure is observed, whereas in all oblique and longitudinal sections, the tubular structure is seen. The dense bands that form the lamellar structures are about 200 Å in thickness, and the less dense interspaces about 350 Å in thickness. The two general patterns observed in thin section depend entirely upon the orientation of the rhabdome with respect to the plane of cutting. The retina of the *Octopus* is at least 1 cm² in area, which means that there would be about 7×10^6 rhabdomeres, equivalent to the number of photo-

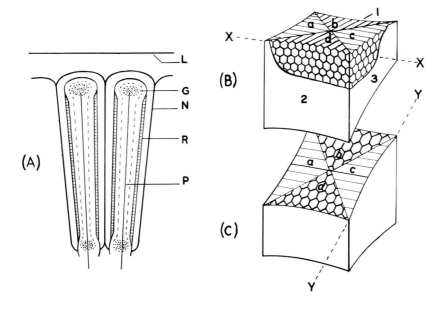

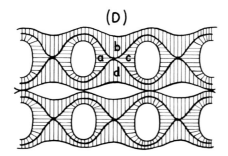

Figure 76 A. A schematic longitudinal section through two rhabdomes. L, limiting membrane; G, pigment granules; N, limiting fiber or membrane;
R, rhabdomere; P, nerve fiber.
B. A cross-section X-X of a three-dimensional view of a single rhabdome
made up of four retinal elements a, b, c, and d.
C. An oblique section Y-Y through the rhabdome showing a lamellar
pattern on sides a and c, packed tubules on the opposite sides b and d.
D. A cross-section of several rhabdomes illustrating the pattern of the
four retinal elements a, b, c, d.

receptors of the vertebrate retina. The surface area available per rhabdomere, assuming that the rhodopsin molecule would be spread as a monolayer over the entire surface, would permit the order of 1×10^9 rhodopsin molecules per rhabdomere.

The orientation of the rhabdomeres in the rhabdome and the internal structure are schematically illustrated in Figure 76, where (A) is a longitudinal cut through several rhabdomes. In (B) and (C) the arrangement of each rhabdomere is depicted depending on whether the cut is through the X-X axis or the Y-Y axis. (D) illustrates how the rhabdomes with their four rhabdomeres appear in cross-section on the surface of the retina (Wolken, 1958b).

It is interesting to note the similarity between *Octopus* and *Sepia* rhabdomeres and those of other arthropods, particularly *Drosophila*, the *Squid* (Zonnana, 1961), and *Pecten*, as well as in an arachnid, the king crab *Limulus* (Miller, 1957), where a similar arrangement of tightly packed tubules has been described (Donnell and Zeutzschel, 1957; Goldsmith and Philpott, 1957; Miller, 1958, 1960; Wolken, 1957; Wolken *et al.*, 1957a, b).

Exner, in 1891, described two anatomically distinct types of compound eye structures, the *apposition* and *superposition* eyes. Figure 65 shows a schematic representation of both types.

In Exner's model, apposition eyes are those in which the photoreceptors, the rhabdomeres that form the rhabdome, lie directly beneath or against the crystalline cone, and in which an inverted image is formed at the level of the receptors, the rhabdome. Each ommatidium is entirely sheathed by a double layer of pigment cells. Only light striking the lens within about 10° of the perpendicular reaches the rhabdomeres. Light striking the lens at a more oblique angle may be reflected by the lens or absorbed by the pigment sheath. Light falling upon the lens of an ommatidium can only reach the rhabdomeres of that ommatidium. There can be no passage of light rays between ommatidia; the rays are restricted to the rhabdomeres of that ommatidium by the pigment sheath. This type of compound eye structure was believed to be characteristic of diurnal insects.

Superposition eyes are those where the receptor cells lie some distance away from the crystalline cone. The extent of the pigment sheath depends upon the degree of dark-adaptation of the eye. In bright light the pigment extends the full length of the ommatidium, as in the apposition eye. However, during dark-adaptation, the pigment granules migrate to the surface of the eye and are drawn up between the crystalline cones, leaving a light-permeable, non-refrac- tile membrane between them. The migration of the pigment granules which are analogous in function to the iris of the vertebrate eye, depends upon the light intensity. At high levels of illumination, the isolation of each ommatidium is nearly perfect, each rhabdome receiving only that light which enters its own ommatidium in a nearly axial direction. At low levels of illumination, the pigment granules are retracted, allowing convergence of light from neighboring ommatidia and consequent brightening of the image.

Thus, light striking the surface of the eye more obliquely is not absorbed by the pigment sheath but passes through to strike the rhabdomeres. In addition, light rays from several ommatidia can be brought to focus upon the rhabdomeres of a single ommatidium, increasing the intensity of the image formed. The superposition eye is a more efficient type. It was believed to be characteristic of nocturnal species, and therefore, the increased light-gathering power of the superposition mechanism was thought to be important. Superposition type eyes have been found in both diurnal and noc- turnal species, however. The diurnal insects, because they do not have the light-gathering problem of the nocturnal insects, usually possess the apposition type, which has not been described in noc- turnal species.

Exner suggested that the crystalline cones of these eyes had lens cylinder properties, the greatest index of refraction being at the axis of the lens cylinder, with concentric rings of decreasing indices of refraction as one proceeded to the periphery of the cone. Such a system would allow for an erect image on the receptor layer and increased light-gathering power, as the light from a point source entering the lenses of several ommatidia could be focused at a single spot on the retina.

There is some question as to whether or not the superposition principle proposed by Exner actually operates in physiological cir- cumstances. There is no evidence of any difference in index of refraction between the center and periphery of the crystalline cone to suggest that the crystalline cone does not have lens cylinder properties. Except for *Lampris,* the superposition principle has not been observed to occur in those eyes that have the superposition structure (a long distance between the crystalline cone and receptor cells). Perhaps the migration of the pigment granules does not function to allow superposition optics in dark-adapted eyes, but rather functions to prevent overstimulation of light-adapted eyes.

A direct correlation has been found between the inter-ommatidial angle and the minimal angle of resolution of alternating black and white strips by insects, which is consistent with the mosaic theory of vision. In the past, observations on resolving power used the optomotor reaction as an exclusive criterion. Recent electrophysiological data, however, demonstrate that the compound eye is capable of resolving an angular separation of far less than the inter-ommatidial angle. The fact that this resolution of alternate strips is found in the ventral nerve cord as well as in the eye, strongly suggests that it may have behavioral significance.

These observations suggest resolving power beyond that possible with an aperture the size of a single ommatidium. Diffraction images of a second and even third order, lying at different depths within the eye and involving the optical interaction of several ommatidia which increases the effective aperture, lead to images which would allow such a fine resolution as has been observed (0.3°). Insect rhabdomeres are peculiar among photoreceptors for their great length; thus the third image is still within the receptor area. To resolve objects of such small angular separation, the retinula cells of an ommatidium would have to function independently. The neurohistology of diptera suggests such independent functioning of retinula cells.

The anatomic separation of the ommatidia of the compound eye suggested that the image the insect sees is a mosaic compound of a number of small images. However, it is now clear that this mosaic theory is inadequate. Recent microscopic and electrophysiological studies have demonstrated that the visual field of an ommatidium is far greater than the ommatidial angle. The fields of adjacent ommatidia clearly overlap. They also suggest that retinula cells function independently. As a light moves across the visual field at any given time, some of the individual cells in an ommatidium "see" the light and some do not, while some retinula cells of adjacent ommatidia also "see" the light and some do not (Kuiper, 1962).

Electron microscopy of the invertebrate retinal cells indicates that there are two geometric arrangements for the rhabdomeres that form the rhabdome. One, a "closed" or fused type, is found in the insects: the cockroach (Fig. 68), the honeybee, grasshopper, locust, dragonfly, moth, and butterfly, where the greater portion of the mesial border and the entire inner margin of the retinula cells are modified to form wedge-shaped rhabdomeres in close proximity with one another around a narrow axial cavity. The other is an "open" type, characteristic of the fruitfly (Fig. 66b), and housefly, in which the rhabdomeres project through a neck-like portion of their retinula cells, extending into a comparatively large axial cavity.

A possible relationship may exist between these two structural arrangements of the "open" and "closed" types and their visual physiology. The action potentials and the electrical response of several arthropod eyes, as investigated by Autrum (1950, 1958), indicate that there are also two physiological types; a "slow" type eye characterized by a negative monophasic potential which is dependent upon the state of dark-adaptation, and a "fast" type eye in which the electroretinogram (ERG) is diphasic, the magnitude and the form of the potential being independent of the state of dark-adaptation. It is of interest, then, that except for the adult dragonflies, all the arthropods having a "closed" arrangement for their rhabdomes possess a "slow" type electrical response. However, all the dipterous and hymenopterous insects that have an "open" type arrangement, possess the "fast" type electrical response. In the "fast" type eye, the rhabdome occupies only a small part of the volume. In the "slow" type eye, characteristic of nocturnal insects which have a light-gathering problem, the rhabdome takes up a much larger part of the volume; for example, the volume of the rhabdome of the cockroach is about five times the volume of the *Drosophila* rhabdome.

One of the interesting problems of animals with compound eyes is the way by which they are able to analyze the direction of vibra-

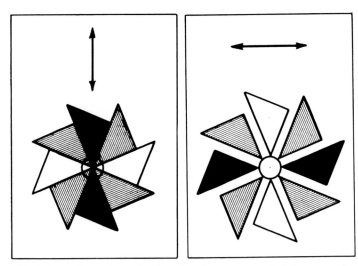

Figure 77 Schematic to show the *fused* and *open* type rhabdomes, and one of
the many possible angles and degree of polarization.

tion of polarized light, using this as a light compass for navigation.
The direction of polarization indicates the relative direction of the
sun. *Drosophila* and the honeybee exhibit orientation relative to
the direction of vibration of polarized light, i.e., they can perceive
the degree of polarization of skylight (Stephens *et al.,* 1953; von
Frisch, 1948), which implies the existence of a polarized light analyzer within the eye. Karl von Frisch (1950, 1953) suggested
that the solution may be in the arrangement and structure of the
visual cells that form the rhabdome. He constructed a model to
show that the rhabdome consists of eight triangular polarizing elements, each transmitting a quantity of light proportional to the
degree of polarization (see Fig. 77 for schematic of "closed" and
"open" type rhabdomes showing the degree of polarization with
respect to the rhabdomeres).

However, polarized light studies indicated that neither the whole
eye nor a single ommatidium acts as the analyzer. The *fine structure* found in the individual rhabdomeres (Figs. 66-69, 71-75) may
indicate that the rhabdomeres are the built-in analyzers of polarized
light (Autrum and Stumpf, 1950; Fernandez-Moran, 1956). The
rhabdomere, as we have described and illustrated, is the only struc-

tural unit found in the compound eye with a parallel rather than a radial symmentry in cross-section. The radial arrangement in the rhabdome of the ommatidium of such radially unsymmetrical units (rhabdomeres) does suggest a relation to the analysis of polarized light in the insect eye.

It has also been proposed that reflection patterns from the environment resolve polarized light into patterns of graded light intensity. According to this view, the compound eye merely discriminates intensity and is not a direct analyzer.

In our laboratory, ants *(Tapinoma sessile, Solenopsis saevissimae)*, houseflies *(Musca domestica)*, fireflies *(Photurus pennsylvanicus)*, and Japanese beetles *(Popillia japonica)* have been shown to orient to plane polarized light under conditions which prevent the use of background reflections as cues for orientation. All the insects studied had a compass reaction (the source of stimulation serves as a fixed point by which an oriented path is maintained) $\pm$ 45° with respect to the plane of polarization of the incident light beam. All oriented at 0 degrees and 90 degrees except the Japanese beetle (Marak and Wolken, 1965).

The use of a white background which reflects normally incident polarized light in a circular pattern, and a black background which reflects elliptically, led to a consistant difference in the response curve. With the white background, there was more orientation at 45 degrees and less at 0 degrees and 90 degrees. This response difference is consistant with the hypothesis that there are more cues for simple phototactic responses on the black background which reflects more light which is perpendicular rather than parallel to the plane of polarization.

Houseflies and fireflies appear to orient to polarized light only within a narrow range of intensities, which is consistent with a model that includes two photoreceptors with different absorption vectors. If these two receptors are oriented at 90 degrees with respect to each other and if the long axis of the visual pigment molecule is oriented in a single plane but free to vibrate in that plane, the receptors will absorb polarized light in a ratio of two to one when the electric vector is parallel to the absorption vector of one of the photoreceptors.

The reflectance pattern of non-polarized light is circular, while the reflectance pattern of polarized light is elliptical, with the long axis perpendicular to the plane of polarization. In normal daylight, the long axis of the ellipse will point to the solar azimuth. This indicates that insect navigation can be accomplished extra-ocularly with little difficulty. However, our understanding of the polarized light analysis, whether intra- or extra- ocular, is at present incomplete.

Chapter VII

INVERTEBRATE EYE PIGMENTS

CHEMICAL ANALYSIS

A COMPLETE ANALYSIS of the eye pigments and the visual pigments of all the invertebrates has not yet been accomplished. The invertebrate photoreceptors have carotenoids, such as β-carotene, which is a precursor to vitamin A and to the synthesis of its aldehyde, retinene, that is necessary for the formation of the visual complex, rhodopsin. Experimental evidence is now accumulating to indicate that invertebrate eyes also possess a retinene$_1$ complex for their visual pigments (Goldsmith and Warner, 1964; Goldsmith *et al.*, 1964).

Let us survey some of these invertebrates, beginning with the eyespot of *Euglena,* since its behavior as a photosensory cell has already been described. It is generally assumed that the eyespot pigment in *Euglena* is the carotenoid, astaxanthin, which was identified in the cytoplasm of the red *Euglena sanguinea.* Astaxanthin (α-hydroxydiketo derivative of β-carotene) is found only in animal tissue and in the eyes and integument of crustaceans. The absorption spectrum of crustacean astaxanthin, unlike those of the plant carotenoids, is a single broad band, maximal in the blue-green, about 500 mμ. There is no evidence that astaxanthin participates in the "rhodopsin cycle" of the vertebrate retina or in the metabolism of vitamin A, but it may function as one of the screening pigments. The identification of astaxanthin in plant cells would be most interesting, for if *Euglena* does contain astaxanthin, it would befit the peculiar biological position of the plant$<$---$>$animal, possessing both the plant pigment, chlorophyll, and the animal pigment, astaxanthin.

Euglena gracilis synthesizes three main carotenoids: β-carotene, lutein, and neoxanthin. Lutein was found as a major pigment and comprises 80 per cent of the total (Goodwin and Jamikorn, 1954). Instead of lutein, however, Krinsky and Goldsmith (1960) found

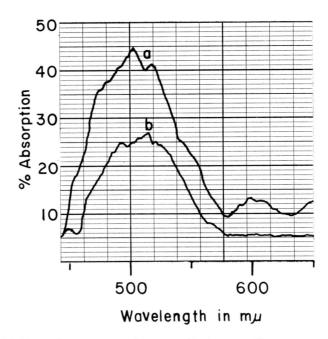

Figure 78 Absorption spectrum of eyespot, *Euglena gracilis;* a. green photosynthetic organism; b. in streptomycin, achlorophyllous mutant. Note similarity of these spectra to carotenoids in Fig. 13b.

antheraxanthin, which accounted for over 80 per cent of the carotenoids, in their analysis. In addition, they found about 11 per cent β-carotene, and 7 per cent neoxanthin, small amounts of γ-carotene, crytoxanthin, echinenone, and two new keto-carotenoids, euglenanone and hydroxy-echinenone.

Using the microspectrophotometer, absorption spectra from 400 to 700 mμ were obtained for single *in vivo Euglena* eyespots of areas of $2\mu^2$. These data (Fig. 78a, b) show that the eyespot has a broad absorption with major peaks in the regions of 480 to 495 mμ and 500 to 530 mμ depending on the environmental state of the organism (Strother and Wolken, 1960b, 1961; Wolken, 1961c). It been indicated that β-carotene could act as a sensitizer in phototropisms (Manten, 1948). When β-carotene, lutein, and neoxanthin are dissolved in light petroleum ether, the absorption peaks lie within the range 415 to 475 mμ. In carbon disulfide, a nonpolar solvent, the range is from 450 to 510 mμ. These carotenoids could therefore account for the major proportion of the absorption in the 400-500 mμ region for the eyespot. These spectra provide some information concerning the nature of the eyespot pigments, and in addition are also useful in connection with observations on the photomotion of *Euglena gracilis* in which the rate of swimming is wavelength-selective (see Figs. 62 and 63). The phototactic responses show absorption peaks in the same range as the eyespot spectra and provide experimental evidence that selective absorption by the eyespot is probably linked to its photomotion (Wolken, 1960a, 1961c; Strother and Wolken, 1961).

Less is known of the photoreceptor pigments of the flatworms *(Platyhelminthes)* and the coelenterates, although action spectra and chemical analysis indicate that carotenoids are also involved. The planarian eye pigments have not been isolated or identified. However, the action spectrum for *Dendrocoelum lacteum* shows two main peaks, one near 510 mμ and another in the ultraviolet near 370 mμ, which is suggestive of the visual pigment, rhodopsin (Pirenne and Marriot, 1955).

Until recently, little was known of the chemistry of the eye pigments of the insects. The insect eyes are capable of forming images and in addition, can distinguish colors. Insects also possess screening and reflecting pigments that serve to regulate the amount of light reaching the sensory cells. According to Nolte (1950), the eye-color pigment in *Drosophila* is contained in four types of cells: two preretinal primary cells found in the crystalline cone; nine secondary cells surrounding the retinula cells; nine basal cells located at the basement membrane; and one post-retinal cell in the outer optic ganglion.

The brown pigments responsible for insect eye color are derived from tryptophan by way of kynurenine and 3-hydroxy-kynurenine (Kikkawa, 1941) and (Butenandt, 1952). It has been postulated that the tryptophan-derived pigments are composed of metallic complex salts, that the pigments are produced by the function of an enzyme having a specific metal as part of its prosthetic group, and that the enzyme function is controlled by a particular gene (Kikkawa *et al.*, 1955).

The method of Kikkawa *et al.* (1955) was followed to determine if there is a difference in the metals associated with the different eye colors of *Drosophila*. Scarlet (st), white (w) and wild-type red-eyed (Canton special) *Drosophila melanogaster,* grown in a temperature controlled room at $25° \pm 2°C.$, were used for these experiments. All flies were at least one week old, so that the pigment concentration in the eyes would be at its maximum (Ephrussi and Herold, 1944).

The heads were removed from scarlet and white-eyed flies and ashed in a crucible at temperatures not exceeding 600°C. The ash was dissolved in .05 N HC1 or double distilled water. A drop of this solution was placed on a strip of Whatman No. 1 filter paper. The solvents used were n-butanol-acetic acid-water (4:1:5) or a solution of acetone-n-butanol-HC1 (10:4:2). The former is useful for detecting iron and copper, and the latter is used in separating copper, cobalt, molybdenum, nickel, and titanium. Two ml. of solvent were placed in the bottom of a graduated cylinder and the cylinder capped until the atmosphere inside became saturated with vapor from the solvent. The chromatographic paper was introduced and the cylinder capped and immersed in an ice bath (15°C.). Adsorption time varied from one to three hours. The chromatographic strips were then removed and dried at room temperature or in an oven at 50°C. The developers, rubeanic acid (0.1 to 0.5% dissolved in 98% ethanol) or potassium ethylxanthogenate (one per cent in double distilled water, were sprayed on the dried papers).

These chromatographs indicated that the scarlet-eye pigmentation is influenced by an iron and/or molybdenum-bearing complex and that the white-eye is controlled by a nickel complex (Wolken *et al.*, 1957b). The red pigments comprising the second pigment system in *Drosophila* eyes have been shown to be pteridines or pteridine derivatives (Forrest and Mitchell, 1954a, b).

Behavioral studies of response to light intensity and wavelength should give an action spectrum indicative of a visual pigment. The phototactic response curves obtained by Fingerman and Brown (1952) indicate that the basic curve for *Drosophila* is that of the white-eyed mutant and that the other response curves differ from this only because of the screening effects of their eye color pigments.

To cancel out the effects of the screening eye-color pigments, the flies were dark-adapted prior to the experiment and in between each determination to make sure that the pigment granules had withdrawn from around the ommatidia.

In determining the action spectrum, the flies were given a choice between two wavelengths, one of which was kept constant, and the other varied. Determinations were made with each type: (1) red filter (626 mμ) constant vs. wavelengths λ_1, λ_2, λ_3 etc., and (2) blue filter (421 mμ) constant vs. wavelengths λ_1, λ_2, λ_3 etc. The distance between the filter windows was 4 cm; the distance of the flies from the light was 4 cm. Equal numbers of males and females were used. The tube was shaken to insure random distribution, and flies were dark-adapted one-half hour prior to the experiments and ten minutes between determinations at each wavelength. The strength of phototaxis was expressed as index of response calculated in relation to a constant index of response for the red filter (625 mμ) or 0.5 to 4.0 for the blue filter (421 mμ).

Response of the flies to a variety of wavelengths presented simultaneously was also determined. The light intensity was adjusted with neutral filters so that the per-cent relative energy was equal at each wavelength (40 foot-candles). Each determination consisted of placing fifty flies of the eye-colored mutant into the experimental tube. The tube was placed in the filter box and the flies were dark-adapted for one-half hour. Approximately equal numbers of males and females were used to assure the response of a normal population. The tube was shaken between each count before the light was turned on.

The response at various wavelengths vs. the two constant wavelengths was measured for the three eye types being studied. The index of response was calculated at λ_1, λ_2, λ_3 etc. to the response at the constant wavelength. The energy required at each wavelength to produce a constant effect, in this case an index of 2.0, was determined from the intensity curves. The reciprocal of the relative energy required to produce an index of response of 2.0 at λ_1, λ_2, λ_3 plotted against wavelength gives an effectiveness spectrum.

For the three eye-color mutants of *Drosophila* investigated, an effectiveness spectra was found, having a maxima at 508 mμ (Fig.79).

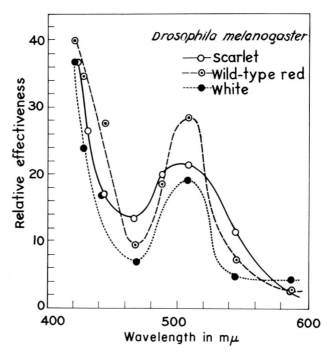

Figure 79 Effectiveness or action spectrum for *Drosophila melanogaster*, three eye type mutants.

Similar action spectra with response peaks at 505 mμ were also obtained for the ant, *Tapinoma sessile*. In all insects investigated (*Drosophila*, ant, housefly, bee), major response peaks were found in the ultraviolet near 365 mμ. Electrophysiological measurements made by Goldsmith (1958b) with the compound eyes of drone bees indicated a peak of sensitivity at 440 mμ.

Fingerman (1952) and Fingerman and Brown (1952, 1953) have demonstrated that *Drosophila* possesses color vision at high light intensities, but at low light intensities there is a "Purkinje shift" from photopic to scotopic vision, similar to vertebrate rod to cone vision, which suggests two types of receptor cells or visual pigments in the eye of *Drosophila*.

To identify the visual pigment in these insects, it was necessary to isolate it from the eyes. This is not an easy task, since thousands of insects must be collected, decapitated, and the pigments extracted

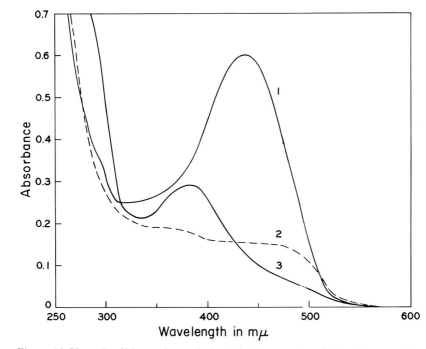

Figure 80 Housefly *(Musca domestica)* absorption spectra of the photosensitive
pigment and the products on bleaching this pigment.

Curve 1 — Eluate (10 ml. eluate P) with 0.2 M phosphate buffer at
pH 6.5, the loaded column previously having been eluted with 15 ml.
of 0.2 M phosphate buffer at pH 7.0 and 10 ml. at pH 6.5.

Curve 2 — Eluate P after bleaching with white light (600 foot-candles
for 2 hours at 12°C).

Curve 3 — 2 ml. of eluate P mixed with 0.3 ml. 2 N KOH and allowed
to stand for 30 minutes in the dark.

from the eyes. From housefly heads *(Musca domestica)*, a light-
sensitive yellow pigment was extracted with phosphate buffer and
was separated from a number of other pigments by chromatography
on calcium phosphate mixed with celite. The procedure was based
on the method described for the purification of cattle rhodopsin
(Bowness, 1959).

Housefly heads (2,000 at a time) were detached from the bodies
by freezing and sieving techniques (Moorefield, 1957). The heads
were then ground in a mortar with 0.05 M NA_2HPO_4: KH_2PO_4

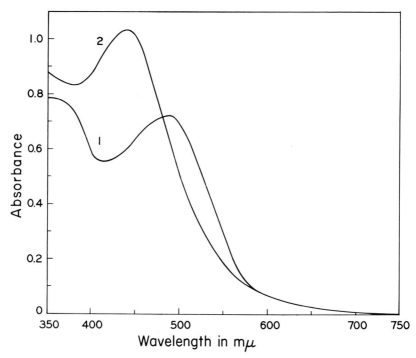

Figure 81 Housefly *(Musca domestica)* absorption of *Curve 1* — A centrifuged extract made with 1 M acetate-acetic acid buffer, pH 4.8 of the top 2 cm. of the extruded calcium phosphate and celite column, the loaded column having been eluted with 15 ml. of phosphate buffer at pH 7.0 and 50 ml. to pH 6.5
Curve 2 — Solution (curve 1) allowed to stand for two hours in the dark.

buffer, pH 7.0 until none could be seen intact. The mixture was frozen to further break up the tissues, allowed to thaw, and centrifuged at 12,000 rpm. for twenty minutes.

The supernatant fraction of the phosphate buffer extract was poured onto a prepared column and the fluid allowed to drain through. Adsorption proceeded best when the solution was diluted to give a 0.025 M buffer concentration. The column was then developed and eluted with 0.2 M phosphate buffer; first 15 ml. at pH 7.0, and then 50 ml. at pH 6.5. The effluent was collected in fractions of 3 ml. each.

After extracting the heads and centrifuging, the supernatant was

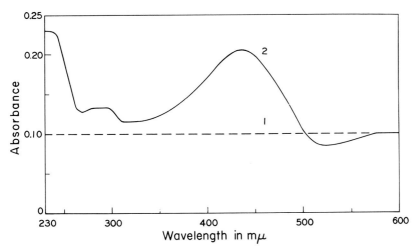

Figure 82 Housefly *(Musca domestica)* Difference spectra obtained by measuring the absorption spectrum of one portion of eluate P of Fig. 80, using, as compensating blank, a bleached portion of the same solution. Curve 1, before, Curve 2, after bleaching the first portion for 10 minutes at 12°C with white light at about 200 foot-candles, while the second portion was kept in the dark at 24°C.

a dark red-brown color. When it was placed on the column, a light yellow fluid drained through. The presence of three other pigments became apparent on eluting with 0.2 M phosphate buffer. A pigment with an absorption peak at about 545 mμ and an inflection at about 515 mμ, and another with a peak at about 408 mμ were evident in the effluent fractions, although they were only obtained mixed with the yellow material. The fourth pigment, the last to come off the column with 0.2 M phosphate buffer, was yellow and light-sensitive and at pH 6.5 had an absorption peak at 437 mμ (Fig. 80). The fraction containing the 437 mμ pigment showed no trace of the absorption maxima of the other three pigments eluted from the column with phosphate buffer. After all the light-sensitive pigment had been eluted, a dark red-brown material, which could be eluted with 2 N KOH, remained at the top of the column. If the pigment was allowed to stay on the column for a day, it turned red, and immediately after elution with 1 M acetate-acetic acid buffer, pH 4.8, showed an absorption peak at 490 mμ that changed to 440 mμ on standing (Fig. 81).

When the photosensitive 437 mμ pigment was bleached by light at pH 6.5 or bleached in the dark at pH 8.0, there was a shift towards longer wavelengths in the 500 to 540 mμ region. In the light at pH 6.5, the main absorption peak was gradually replaced by a plateau of absorption around 440 to 460 mμ. In solutions at pH 8.0, peaks at 250 and 290 mμ were very pronounced. Difference spectra gave a curve with maxima at 432 mμ and a broader band from 280-290 mμ (Fig. 82).

Goldsmith (1958a, b) has also shown that a photosensitive pigment is present in phosphate buffer extracts of honeybee heads. Partial purification of the extracts indicated that a retinene$_1$-protein complex was present with an absorption maximum at 440 mμ. The absorption maximum of 437 mμ of the light-sensitive housefly pigment at pH 6.5 lies very close to that of the honey bee pigment. Retinene$_1$ was also found by M.H. Briggs in bumble bees (New Zealand), and the grasshopper. Retinene was found only in the heads of these insects and not in any other parts of their bodies.

These findings, that retinene$_1$ occurs in the heads of certain insects, raised many questions about the insect visual pigments. Retinene is formed in the vertebrate eye by the oxidation of vitamin A, which is apparently not required by insects, for there has been no adequate evidence that vitamin A occurs in the bodies of insects other than in the heads.

It is of interest to note a number of similarities in spectroscopic properties between the insect pigment and the visual pigments which have been found in many animals (Wald, 1955, 1959; Dartnall, 1957). First, there are the pH indicator properties shown by the light-sensitive housefly pigment and by its bleached products. On bleaching in the light at pH 6.5, a solution with plateaus of absorption at 440 to 460 mμ and 350 to 360 mμ is produced. Addition of a strong acid to this material gives a plateau or a peak at 470 to 475 mμ. In alkaline solution there is a plateau at 360 mμ only. Absorption maxima in these three wavelength regions are given by the retinylideneamines and indicator-yellow under similar conditions of pH (Ball *et al.*, 1949; Collins, 1954), although the 440 mμ form of retinylideneamines is not stable except at pH 1 (Morton and Pitt, 1955). An absorption maximum at 380 mμ is produced at pH 12 with the housefly pigment. A peak at this wavelength is obtained with *Squid* metarhodopsin at pH 9.9, and from cattle metarhodopsin at pH 13 (Hubbard and Kropf, 1959a, b). Second, the bleaching process of the housefly pigment, as with the visual pigments (Wald, 1955), appears to involve more than one stage.

There are a number of observations which indicate that protein may be a part of the light-sensitive housefly pigment. First, the ultraviolet absorption spectrum of the pigment, either bleached or unbleached, exhibited a peak at 290 mμ in alkaline solution. Most proteins show a peak at 290 mμ in alkaline solution, though in neutral or acid solution they have a similar peak at 275 to 280 mμ (Beaven and Holiday, 1952). Second, the heat bleaching of the pigment at 100°C. gave a coagular precipitate, which when dissolved in 0.2 N sodium hydroxide, showed a peak at about 290 mμ. Third, a precipitate containing about 10.5 per cent nitrogen was obtained from the light-sensitive pigment solution upon addition of sulfosalicylic acid.

The absorption spectrum of the light yellow pigment which drained through the column with 0.025 M phosphate buffer appears to be of the melanin type. The red pigment, which required 2 N KOH or 1 M acetate-acetic acid buffer at pH 4.8 for elution from the column, exhibited a shift in absorption maximum from about 490 to 440 mμ in changing from alkaline to acid conditions (Fig. 81). This is similar to the shift shown by rhodommatin, a red pigment obtained from insects by Butenandt *et al.* (1954), which possibly is related to the pteridines (Forrest and Mitchell, 1954b).

One of the pigments obtained from *Drosophila* by Wald and Allen (1946) had an absorption maximum at 436 mμ. No light sensitivity was reported for this pigment; the absorption curve resembles the 440 mμ form of the pigment shown in Fig. 81 curve 2 rather than the light-sensitive housefly pigment.

Procedures involving a larger number of heads (4,000) were used to identify retinene$_1$ more specifically. Three different methods were used. First, the heads were completely ground in a mortar and pestle with anhydrous sodium sulfate and acetone. The mixture was centrifuged at 2000 rpm and the supernatant poured off and retained. The residue was re-extracted with acetone, and after centrifuging, the supernatant was combined with the first extract. This was repeated until all the color was removed.

The second method was to grind the heads with 80 ml. 0.2 M phosphate buffer, pH 6.5 and to centrifuge this mixture at 12,000 rpm for twenty minutes. The residue was extracted with acetone, while the supernatant was fractionated by saturation with ammonium sulfate at 45 per cent and 60 per cent, and the ammonium sulfate precipitates were extracted with acetone.

The third method was to grind the heads with 20 ml. of 50 per cent sucrose in m/15 phosphate buffer, pH 6.5 and then centrifuge the sucrose mixture at 3000 rpm./min. for ten minutes. The residue was extracted with acetone, while the supernatant suspension was diluted with phosphate buffer to a sucrose concentration of 12.5 per cent and centrifuged at 14,000 rpm. for twenty minutes. The sedimented material was then extracted with acetone.

The initial acetone extract from each of the above preparations was evaporated to dryness, and the residue was dissolved in petroleum ether. The petroleum ether extract was then dried over anhydrous sodium sulfate, evaporated to dryness, redissolved in petroleum ether and chromatographed on alumina (Fisher Adsorption Alumina, 80-200 mesh). The alumina was weakened by exposing it to a water-saturated atmosphere and allowing it to adsorb with 5 g. water/100 g. alumina. The first column was eluted with 40 ml. of 40 per cent acetone in petroleum ether (v/v). The eluate was evaporated to dryness, redissolved in petroleum ether, and applied to a second column; fractions were eluted with 4 per cent, 17.5 per cent, 25 per cent, and 40 per cent acetone in petroleum ether (v/v). The effluent fractions were evaporated to dryness, then stored in a vacuum dessicator in the dark. The acetone extracts of the precipitate from the ammonium sulfate fractionation (procedure 2) and the extract of the material which sedimented in 12.5 per cent sucrose solution (procedure 3), were evaporated to dryness and dissolved in chloroform.

The results of the chromatograms of an acetone extract of the housefly heads showed a separation of one or more of the carotenoids present. Of the various carotenoids obtained, retinene$_1$ can be identified. The fraction eluted with 25 per cent acetone in petroleum

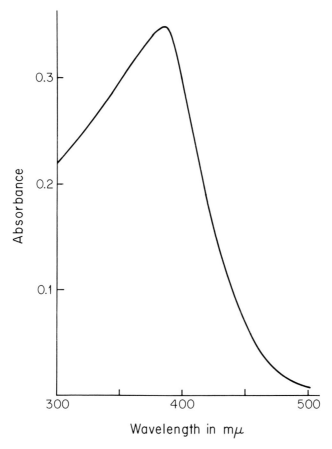

Figure 83 Housefly *(Musca domestica)* eye extract. Absorption spectrum of the retinene-containing fraction in chloroform.

ether had an absorption maximum at 385 mμ in chloroform (Fig. 83), and, when reacted with antimony trichloride (a transient blue color), a maximum absorption at 665 mμ was observed. Spectra of the material removed by sucrose and phosphate buffer treatments showed similar results.

The amount of retinene present in the housefly heads may be estimated by comparison with the known $E_{1cm}^{1\%}$ value for retinene in the antimony trichloride reaction (Ball *et al.*, 1949), which gives a figure of 0.31 μg of retinene/g fresh weight of heads. From the

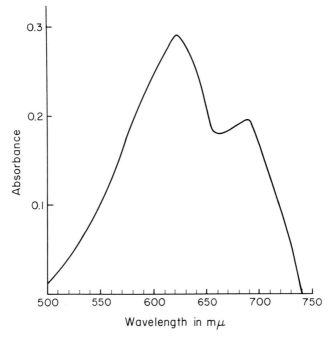

Figure 84 Housefly *(Musca domestica)* eye extract. Absorption spectrum of antimony trichloride reaction of fraction eluted with 17.5% acetone in petroleum ether (v/v) showing maxima at 623 and 693 mμ.

average number of 24,500 rhabdomeres per eye (Fernández-Morán, 1958) this corresponds to 2.7×10^7 molecules of retinene per rhabdomere.

The presence of retinene$_1$ in the extract indicates that vitamin A should also be present, since, in the visual cycle, retinene$_1$ is reduced to vitamin A$_1$. Solutions with an absorption band at about 328 mμ were obtained after bleaching the 437 mμ housefly pigment, adding ethanol, evaporating to dryness, and extracting with chloroform. A transient blue color was obtained when antimony trichloride was added to some extracts made this way. Vitamin A$_1$ has a principal absorption maxima at 328 mμ, and it gives a blue color with a peak at 620 mμ. Fractions were obtained whose antimony trichloride tests gave maxima near 620 and 696 mμ, the maxima for vitamins A$_1$ and A$_2$; in some cases, these were found in the same fraction

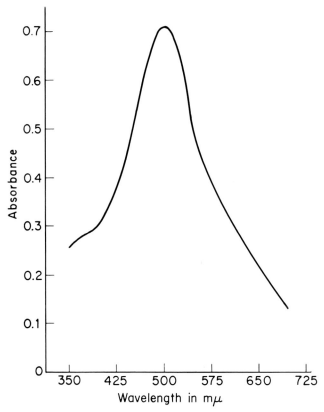

Figure 85 Absorption spectrum of the cockroach *(Blatta orientalis)* rhabdomere fraction extracted with 1.8% aqueous digitonin, pH 7.0 M/15 phosphate buffer.

(Fig. 84). The identification of vitamin A_2 is particularly crucial, since it is so far known to occur only in fresh-water fish and in some amphibians, and this would be the first instance of its presence outside these vertebrate groups (Fig. 102).

Of the other fractions eluted from the column, two contained light-stable carotenoids. The fraction eluted with 4 per cent acetone in petroleum ether was yellow in color, and its absorption spectrum in chloroform showed maxima at 486, 455, and 426 $m\mu$. These maxima correspond closely with those of lutein (a plant xanthophyll).

To see if the cockroach eye pigment would also contain retinene₁, one group of cockroach heads was ground with 40 ml. of 45 per cent

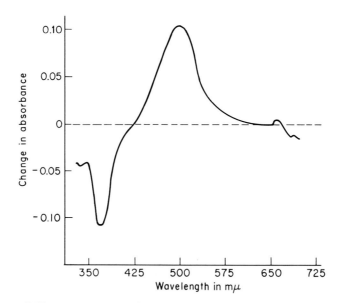

Figure 86 Difference spectrum of the cockroach *(Blatta orientalis)* eye pigment (Fig. 85) after exposure to white light.

sucrose in pH 9.0 m/15 phosphate buffer to make a thin paste. The paste was then transferred to centrifuge tubes, layered over with phosphate buffer at pH 7.0 and centrifuged in a Spinco preparative ultracentrifuge at 100,000 × g for twenty minutes. The supernatant, containing most of the rhabdomeres, was drawn off, and the sediment was reground with 20 ml. of sucrose solution and fractionated again as already described. The supernatants were combined, diluted with 1000 ml. of buffer solution, and centrifuged in a chilled rotor (0°C.) at 25,000 × g for forty minutes. The sediment was taken up in 100 ml. of fresh buffer and left in the dark at 6°C. for fifteen hours. The suspension was then centrifuged and the residue was taken up in 10 ml. of distilled water and lyophilized. The dry powder was extracted twice in the dark with 300 ml. of petroleum ether and dried again by evaporation. The defatted dry powder was then extracted at room temperature (25°C.) for three hours with 5 ml. of 1.8 per cent digitonin in pH 7.0 m/15 phosphate buffer. The pigment extract was centrifuged for forty minutes at 18,000 × g. in a chilled rotor (0°C.) to clarify the solution. No further purification of this fraction was carried out.

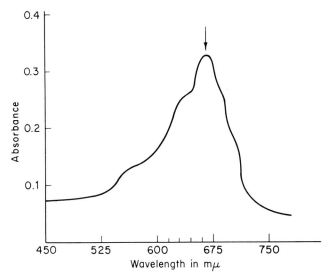

Figure 87 Cockroach *(Blatta orientalis)* eye pigment. Absorption spectrum of the fraction chromatographed on alumina column, eluted with 17.5% acetone in petroleum ether and reacted with antimony trichloride. The arrow indicates absorption maximum at 664 mμ.

The absorption spectrum of the cockroach eye fraction extracted with 1.8 per cent aqueous digitonin has its major peak at approximately 500 mμ (Fig. 85). The difference spectrum (Fig. 86) shows a maximum at 500 mμ, corresponding to a rhodopsin, and a minimum at 375 mμ, corresponding to retinene. The bleached spectrum also shows a shift in the maximum from approximately 500 mμ to 375 mμ, which is indicative of the uncoupling of retinene from the opsin of rhodopsin in light bleaching. A similar spectral shift can be obtained by adding hydroxylamine to rhodopsin, which at room temperature, combines very rapidly with retinene in aqueous solution and yields a retinene oxime (Wald, 1956).

Another group of cockroach heads was ground in a mortar and pestle with five times its weight of anhydrous sodium sulfate. The mixture was extracted repeatedly with petroleum ether in the dark at 10°C. The residue was then extracted in the light at room temperature 25°C., with 250 ml. of acetone containing 6 per cent ethanol and 4 per cent water. The acetone extract was evaporated to dryness under reduced pressure, taken up in 10 ml. of petroleum

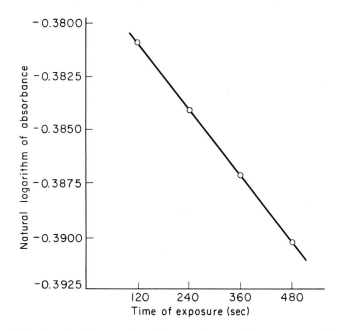

Figure 88 Cockroach *(Blatta orientalis)* eye pigment. Time course of bleaching of the photosensitive pigment.

ether, and placed on a column of alumina which had been wetted with water to 5 per cent of its dry weight. The column was eluted first with 100 ml. of petroleum ether and then with mixtures of acetone in petroleum ether varying from 4 to 40 per cent (v/v). The effluents from the columns were evaporated to dryness and dissolved in 1 ml. of chloroform.

The chromatographic fractions eluted from the alumina columns in acetone also show absorption spectra indicative of retinene. The fraction eluted with 17.5 per cent acetone in petroleum ether, when reacted with antimony trichloride, gives an absorption maximum at 664 mμ which is characteristic of retinene$_1$ (Fig. 87).

The time course of bleaching follows first-order kinetics since the plot of the natural logarithm of the absorbancy of the pigment-complex against the time of exposure to light yields a straight line (Fig. 88). The first-order rate constant obtained from the slope of this line is 6.1 $\times$ 10^{-5} sec^{-1} at 25°C.

The spectral characteristics of the pigment complex of the cock-roach are comparable to rhodopsins extracted from marine inverte-brate eyes, for example: the cephalopod molluscs *Loligo* (Bliss, 1948; St. George and Wald, 1949; Hubbard and St. George, 1958); *Octopus* and *Sepia* (Brown and Brown, 1958); the crustacean, *Homarus* (Wald and Hubbard, 1957); three species of euphausiids (Kampa, 1955); and the arachnid, *Limulus* (Hubbard and Wald, 1960), all such were found to possess a retinene$_1$-protein complex, a rhodopsin.

The cockroach pigment extract differs in absorption maximum and in solubility from the pigments extracted from the housefly and the honeybee which are soluble in phosphate buffer and show maxima at 437 and 440 mμ (Bowness and Wolken, 1959; Goldsmith, 1958a).

Electrophysiological studies of the cockroach eye (Walther, 1958; Walther and Dodt, 1959) show a maximum sensitivity peak at 507 mμ. Studies of the ocellus of the cockroach *Periplaneta ameri-cana*, indicated a single photoreceptor with a maximum also at about 500 mμ (Goldsmith and Ruck, 1958). In addition, Walther (1958) suggested that the cockroach eye contains two types of photore-ceptor; the lower half of the eye containing one type with the absorption maximum at 507 mμ, and the upper half containing both types, one at 507 mμ and another with maximum sensitivity be-tween 314 and 369 mμ. Electrophysiological studies of the eyes of honeybees show that they, too, have a complicated system involving several photoreceptors with maximum sensitivities in different regions of the spectrum (Goldsmith, 1958b, 1961).

However, we have isolated only one photosensitive pigment com-plex from the compound eye of the cockroach (Wolken and Scheer, 1963). It is therefore more likely that the structure and arrangement of the lens, which is known to play a significant role in determining the sensitivity of the eye to light in the near ultraviolet region (Wald, 1945; Dodt and Walther, 1958; Buriain and Ziv, 1959), together with the rhodosin bleaching characteristics (Wald and Brown, 1958), could account for the dual sensitivity of the cockroach eye.

To calculate the concentration of rhodopsin, we have used the known absorbancy of a 1 per cent solution (w/v) of retinene$_1$ in a 1 cm light path (3400) in the antimony trichloride reaction. The amount of retinene per gram of cockroach heads (fresh tissue weight) was found to be 0.08 μg. Similar analyses and calculations for other insects studied gave values of 0.31 μg for the housefly (Wolken, Bowness, and Scheer, 1960) and 0.22 μg for the honeybee (Goldsmith, 1958a). On the basis of 28,000 rhabdomeres per eye (Wolken and Gupta, 1961), the amount of retinene per rhabdomere was calculated to be 4.3 $\times$ 10^7 molecules.

All of the pigments previously extracted from the eyes of insects differ from typical rhodopsins in absorption characteristics and in solubility. The pigment isolated from the honeybee by Goldsmith (1958a), although possessing retinene$_1$ as a chromophore, is phosphate buffer soluble, whereas vertebrate rhodopsin and the rhodopsins isolated from other invertebrates require the use of a solubilizing agent (e.g., digitonin) for extraction. In addition, the absorption maximum of this pigment lies at 440 mμ, rather than in the neighborhood of 500 mμ. Since retinene seems to be found in all visual receptors, differences in the solubility and spectral properties of visual pigments indicate the possibility that the proteins of the visual complex of the invertebrate differ from those of the vertebrate rhodopsins and that there is a difference in this respect among invertebrates, too. Thus, the cockroach probably possesses a rhodopsin-like visual complex which is more comparable to that found in some marine invertebrates (e.g., *Octopus, Sepia, Limulus*) and in vertebrates.

We can now begin to see how the carotenoids of the visual complex may fit into a universal scheme of photoexcitation for all animals possessing eyes (Fig. 102).

Chapter VIII

MOLECULAR STRUCTURE OF
THE VERTEBRATE ROD

THE FUNDAMENTAL problem in visual excitation, then, is to understand how the action of light on a visual pigment, in such highly organized photoreceptor structures as the rods and cones, leads to nervous excitation.

From this survey of the structure and pigments of the vertebrate and invertebrate photoreceptors, we can return to the molecular anatomy of the vertebrate retina. The *fine structure* of retinal rod and cone outer segments has been observed as being stacked plates or discs, having a repeat unit of the order of 250 Å. Each plate or disc is probably a double layer with additional *fine structure*. These stacked plates or discs resemble the highly ordered structure of crystals.

The principal components of the retinal rods are pigment, protein, and lipids. In terms of wet weight, the visual pigment, rhodopsin, accounts for 4 to 10 per cent, lipids for 20 to 40 per cent, and the proteins for 40 to 50 per cent. For example, cattle rhodopsin constitutes 3.6 per cent of the rod wet weight, and 13 per cent of the dry weight. Frog rhodopsin, however, is 10 per cent of the rod wet weight and more than 35 per cent of its dry weight. Calculations from spectroscopic data show that there are of the order of 3×10^9 rhodopsin molecules per frog rod and 4×10^6 rhodopsin molecules per cattle retinal rod.

The precise location of the pigment, lipid, and protein within the rod structure is not known, but has been assumed with fixing agents and with various stains from the chemical reactions of the tissue. More specific identification of the rhodopsin molecules within the lamellae of the rods is being sought by use of histochemical methods and specific stains, combined with high resolution electron microscopy.

[141]

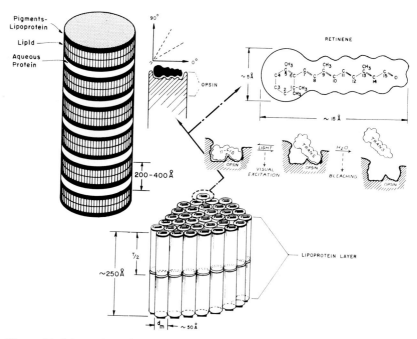

Figure 89 Schematic molecular model for a retinal rod outer segment, showing the layers in molecular dimensions and the orientation of rhodopsin in these layers. Note the complex of retinene with opsin to form rhodopsin and its uncoupling after bleaching with light (after Hubbard, 1954).

To visualize a structural molecular model for the retinal rod outer segment, the geometry (number of lamellae, length, diameter, and thickness) was measured and tabulated from numerous electron micrographs (see Table VIII). Applying this data on geometry and pigment concentration, the surface area and the volume that the rhodopsin molecule would occupy in relation to the number of lamellae and their total surface area in the retinal rod outer segment can be calculated (Wolken, 1961a, 1962b, 1963).

The dense layers (lamellae) are probably double layers that are structurally represented as lipid-lipoprotein, with the low molecular weight lipids occupying the interstitial spaces. It is assumed that monomolecular layers of pigment molecules are at the lipoprotein-lipid layer interfaces, and that these layers are separated by aqueous protein layers as indicated in the schematic model (Fig. 89).

The cross-sectional area A, which would be associated with each macromolecule and therefore with each rhodopsin molecule, is

$$A = \frac{\pi D^2}{4P}$$

where D is the diameter of the photoreceptor and P is the number of pigment molecules in a single monolayer. The maximum cross-sectional area A for each rhodopsin molecule can be derived from the above equation, where P is replaced by N/2n, in which N is the pigment concentration in molecules per retinal rod and n is the number of dense layers per outer segment:

$$A = \frac{\pi D^2 n}{N} .$$

The cross-sectional areas calculated for cattle and frog rhodopsin are then 2500 Å^2 and 2620 Å^2, respectively (Table VIII). The diameter of the rhodopsin molecule would be of the order of 50 Å which is about the right order of magnitude. It has been estimated that the rhodopsin molecule (cattle, frog), if spherical, would have a diameter of the order of 40 Å (Wald, 1954).

The size of the rhodopsin molecule indicates that there would be sufficient space for all of the rhodopsin molecules to fit over all of the lamellar surfaces. A small area is enlarged in Figure 89 to show how the rhodopsin molecules (retinene + opsin) are packed in the dense double layered lamellae. This shows that there would be one retinene molecule per opsin molecule to form the rhodopsin complex (Hubbard and Kropf, 1959b; Wolken, 1961a).

The rhodopsin molecular weight M has been calculated from the structural model and the rhodopsin concentration, where D is the diameter of the photoreceptor; T is the thickness of the dense layers; s is taken as 1.3 the density of the protein, (if a lipoprotein, the density would be closer to 1.1); L is Avogadro's number 6×10^{23}; n is the number of dense layers; and N is the number of pigment molecules per photoreceptor.

$$M = \frac{\pi D^2 TsLn}{4N} .$$

The molecular weights calculated from the above equation for frog and cattle rhodopsin are 60,000 and 40,000 respectively (Wolken, 1962b). The molecular weight estimated for rhodopsin extracts (Table VIII) obtained from their analysis and sedimentation in the

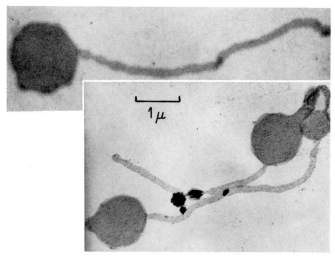

Figure 90 Frog retinal rod sonicated (20,000 cps for 5 sec) fixed immediately with 1% OsO_4, washed and dried. Electron micrograph.

analytical ultracentrifuge for frog rhodopsin was 67,000 (Wolken, 1961a) and for cattle rhodopsin 40,000 (Hubbard, 1954). These estimates, then, whether obtained from the model or the rhodopsin extract, are in agreement (Table VIII).

To see if there is a "visual unit" of a minimum number of rhodopsin molecules necessary for light capture and hence, excitation, the retinal rods were sonicated in an ice bath for periods of time varying from 5 seconds to 45 minutes at 20,000 cps. to unravel the lamellar discs (Fig. 90). The sonicated retinal material was sprayed on electron microscope grids and negatively stained using 5 per cent solution of uranyl acetate, pH 3.8, and 1 per cent phosphotungstic acid PTA. Some of the grids were shadowed with palladium. Frog retinal rods sonicated for 10 minutes showed particles about 0.2μ in diameter (Figs. 91 and 92) whose absorption spectra (Fig. 92b, curve 1) and difference spectrum (the bleached curve 2 from the unbleached curve 1 results in curve 3), the spectrum for rhodopsin. These particles still contain rhodopsin. These negative stained particles appear as aggregates of regularly packed globular subunits of the order of 40 to 50 Å in diameter (Fig.

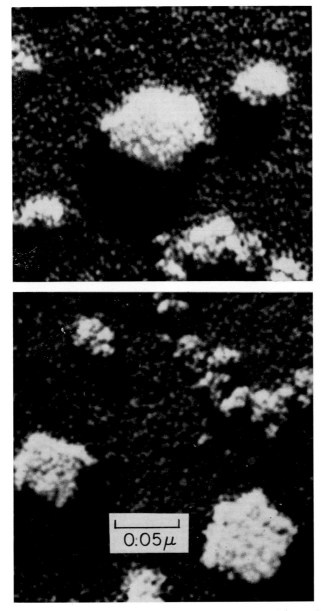

Figure 91 Frog retinal rods, sonicated (20,000 cps for 10 min) particles negatively stained; electron micrograph.

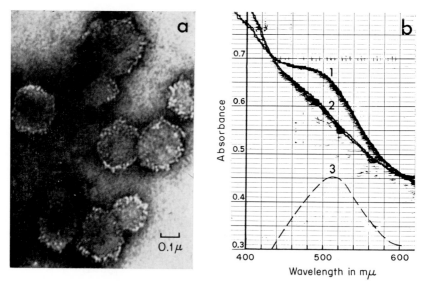

Figure 92a Sonicated frog rods (20,000 cps for 10 minutes) negatively stained; electron micrograph.

   b. Absorption spectrum of sonicated particles curve 1, bleached particles curve 2, the difference spectrum curve 3, shows that these particles contain the visual pigment, rhodopsin.

91 and 92a) which are within the size calculated for the rhodopsin molecules. Each of these particles ($\sim 0.3\mu$) would contain of the order of a thousand rhodopsin molecules. Human retinal rods, fixed and thin-sectioned, show lamellar globules (50Å) of similar size (Fig. 93). Until more precise experimental data is obtained, our estimate that the rhodopsin molecule is of the order of 50 Å in diameter and of a molecular weight of the order of 50,000 seems to be fairly reliable. It should be pointed out, however, that the major part of the molecular weight of rhodopsin is due to the protein, opsin, and that different species probably also have different proteins.

The molecular structure for the retinal rods and cones, as we view it, is a convenient method by which a membrane could be rolled up in an ordered fashion, providing a large surface area for the number of rhodopsin molecules required by compressing a large surface area into a small volume (Fig. 94).

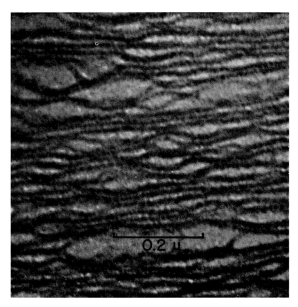

Figure 93 Human retinal rod outer segment at high resolution, showing the lamellae and globules (50 Å diameter) within them.

Periodic Structures

What kind of properties, structural and otherwise, does rhodopsin possess? Rhodopsin is an aqueous (1-2 percent digitonin) extract of the retinal rods. It was fortunate that all of the photochemistry of rhodopsin was carried out in aqueous digitonin solution. Digitonin is a non-ionic detergent that forms colloid aggregates, micelles, in solution. It also has a large dye binding capacity for carotenoids. Each micelle consists of about 75 molecules and has a minimum molecular weight of about 75,000 (Fig. 95). It was estimated from ultracentrifuge sedimentation data that there are probably three such micelle aggregates with a molecular weight of the order of 225,000 (Hubbard, 1954).

It was suggested that the role of the detergent (digitonin) micelle in reacting with one of the substrates, simultaneously attracting the other substrate to the same vicinity, parallels the behavior of an enzyme in bringing the reactants together (Lowe and Phillips, 1961). Extracted rhodopsin possesses photochemical activity (light $<--->$

TABLE VIII

STRUCTURAL DATA: RETINAL ROD OUTER SEGMENTS

Average Measurements

Animal	D Diameter	T Thickness of dense layers	n Number of dense layers per photorepector	N Number of rhodopsin molecules per photoreceptor	A Cross-sectinal area of rhodopsin	d_M Diameter of rhodopsin molecule	M Calculated molecular weight pigment-complex
	(μ)	(Å)			(Å^2)	(Å)	
Frog	5.0	150	1000	3.8×10^9	2620	51	60,000
Cattle	1.0	200	180	4.2×10^6	2500	50	40,000

Data taken from Wolken (1961a).

dark reactions) similar to the intact retinal rod. Analysis of the extracted rhodopsin shows it to have retinene, protein, and lipid in the same relative concentrations as in the retinal rod. Since the rhodopsin micelles (in digitonin) are of the order of 300,000 molecular weight and also possess liquid-crystalline properties (Wolken, 1961a, 1962b), the rhodopsin molecules become aligned as visualized in Figure 95. This kind of structure is observed when a drop of rhodopsin is rapidly evaporated from solution, forming periodic ring structures (Fig. 96a). Analysis of the rings and interspaces by scanning with the microspectrophotometer shows that the α and β absorption peaks of rhodopsin at 500 and 355 mμ are located in the rings, whereas the interspaces have a high absorption at 280 mμ. Since no attempt was made to prevent bleaching of these preparations, the absorption maximum for retinene at 385 mμ is used to illustrate the scan in the rings and interspaces (Fig. 96b). In addition, such a structure indicates the quasi-crystalline nature of the

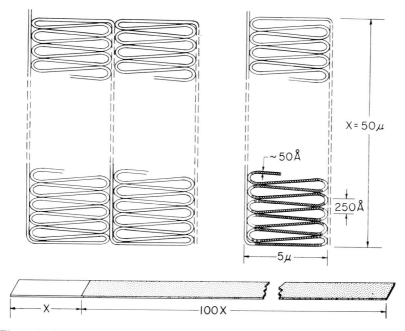

Figure 94 Schematic representation of how the lamellae could be formed for the rods and cones.

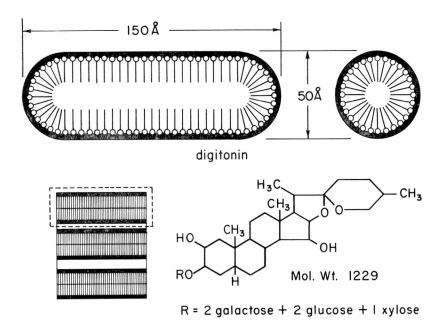

digitonin

Mol. Wt. 1229

R = 2 galactose + 2 glucose + 1 xylose

Figure 95 The molecular structure, schematic molecular model of a digitonin micelle, showing three such micelles aggregated.

rhodopsin micelles and has analogies to the molecular structure of the retinal rod outer segment (as in Figs. 32b and 34).

The interpretation of the highly ordered lamellar structure of the retinal photoreceptors must be that it provides for the orientation of the photosensitive rhodopsin and that its molecular structure is an efficiency mechanism for light capture; hence, critical for function.

Dispersions of the photoreceptor complex exhibit transition phases. If the lipid-lipoprotein-water systems of photoreceptors displayed similar properties, the phase transitions of the lipid (melting and crystallization of the paraffins chains) would cause drastic changes in the selective permeability to cations, and could play a role in the excitation if selective permeability in the membranes of the outer rod segments is involved. Osmium tetroxide (OsO_4), the fixative used, preserves some liquid-crystalline phases of soaps and phospholipids to the extent that it is possible to observe their structure by electron microscopy.

What kind of systems give rise to periodic structures as found

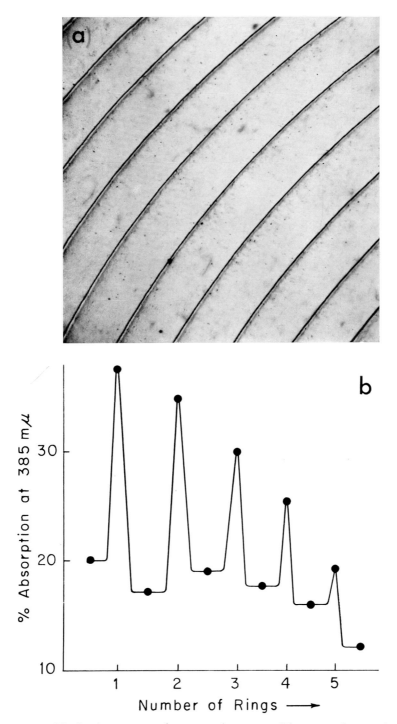

Figure 96a Rhodopsin evaporated on a microscope slide; note the regular
periodic pattern. X 120

b. Microspectrophotometric scan at 385 mμ to show that retinene is
found in the rings and not in the interspaces.

for the photoreceptors? It is of interest here to indicate several experiments on the formation of periodic structures. One is the Liesegang ring phenomena; this was observed by Liesegang in the course of staining specimens for histological study by the Golgi technique i.e., the impregnation of potassium dichromate and silver nitrate into tissue. Liesegang's experiments and theories to explain the phenomena are given by Hedges (1932) and in a more recent review by Stern (1954). The formation of the ring structures can be observed when a drop of 15 per cent silver nitrate is placed on a sheet of gelatin which has previously been impregnated with about 0.4 per cent potassium dichromate. The silver slowly diffuses into the gelatin, there it reacts with the potassium dichromate, and a silver dichromate complex is precipitated in a periodic manner. The precipitation is not continuous but forms a series of orange-red concentric rings separated by clear spaces in the gel (Fig. 97). Another example of the same phenomena is that of gelatin saturated with ferric chloride; if a drop of potassium ferrocyanide solution is placed in the center, blue rings of ferri-ferrocyanide are formed. Light can modify these periodic structures, if the precipitated molecular complexes are light sensitive.

Periodic structures are also formed when salts crystallize out in colloids or proteins. An example of such periodic crystallization is that of potassium dichromate in gelatin. The procedure is to place a drop of saturated potassium dichromate in gelatin solution on a microscope slide, warm gently, and quickly transfer the slide to the microscope. It will be observed that crystallization begins around the periphery of the drop and proceeds by periods of rapid and slow growth. The distance between the rings decreases with the thickness of the film and with increasing rate of crystallization. The crystallization of sodium chloride is also affected by extremely small concentrations of most proteins (i.e., serum); as the ions are absorbed on the surface, the sodium chloride molecules are deposited in fine crystals on the glass surface, and at certain salt concentrations, periodic rings are formed (Lecomte de Noüy, 1926).

Now let us return to digitonin, used for extracting rhodopsin. Its specific configuration permits combination with free cholestrol and with other natural sterols in the free state. Digitonin exhibits

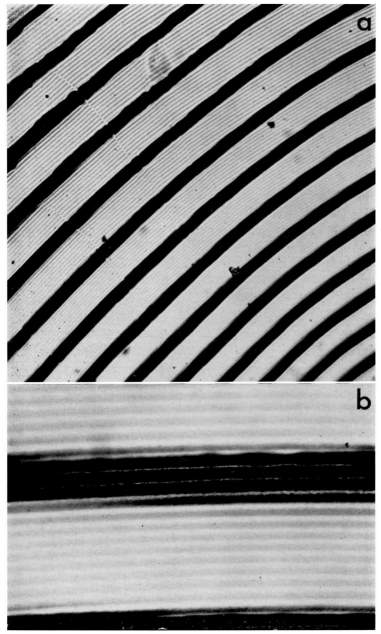

Figure 97 Liesegang ring structure. 15% silver nitrate dropped into gelatin
saturated with potassium dichromate.
  a. Low magnification. X 60
  b. High magnification. X 200.

paracrystalline properties; when evaporated from a drop of solution on a surface, periodic rings form. If a dye such as methylene blue, chlorophyll, or retinene is added to the digitonin solution and the same experiment is carried out, the dye will then be found concentrated in the rings (as in Fig. 96a; Wolken, 1960b, 1961a).

Liquid crystals are generally divided into the smectic and nematic paracrystalline states. The more highly ordered of these is the smectic, where the molecules are arranged in equidistant parallel layers. Robinson and Ward (1957) have shown that when the L and D forms of the polypeptide, polybenzoylglutamate, are mixed in dioxane, they behave as a liquid crystal. Although the solution was birefringent, no regular orientation was observed with the polarizing microscope, but after a short time, orientation appeared on the walls of the capillary and spread toward the center. If digitonin is made to flow through a capillary, when observed through crossed polaroids, it becomes birefringent. Rhodopsin also becomes birefringent when made to flow through a capillary.

Quantitative theories have tried to explain the formation of liquid crystals as resulting from the anisotropic interaction between long, rod-like molecules. These theories indicate the essential feature that, if too many long rods are packed in a given space, they pack very poorly unless they are aligned; if aligned they can be packed more economically. Hence, a concentrated solution of rod-like molecules tends to form liquid crystal structures, but, if diluted, isotropic structures occur (Zimm, 1959).

These experiments would indicate that the extracted rhodopsin molecules become aligned in the digitonin micelles that have properties of a liquid crystal. Such a structure is concentration-dependent and temperature-dependent. Because of this behavior, the structural integrity of the rod is maintained.

We visualize, then, that the orientation of rhodopsin in the digitonin micelles (Fig. 96a) is similar to that of rhodopsin in the retinal rod (Figs. 32b and 34) and that a liquid crystal type of matrix is necessary for orientation of the photosensitive rhodopsin molecules.

Structure and Energy Transfer

The highly ordered molecular structure of the photoreceptors has analogies to the lattice structure of crystals, which has led to the idea that it bears a close relation to a solid state system, i.e., exhibiting such properties of the solid state as electronic energy transfer or electronic charge transfer. In electronic energy transfer, light energy absorbed by one pigment molecule raises the molecule to an excited state. The excitation energy may disappear from the first molecule and reappear on another molecule some distance away. This transfer of energy can continue until the energy lands on a molecule in a position to trigger the signal. In electronic charge transfer, the first molecule that absorbs the light releases an electronic charge, which can move away from the original site if an electric field is present, making an electric current. Since the current is caused by the absorption of light, the process is called photoconductivity.

In the formation of a charge transfer complex, the molecules must be brought together, which can be done by (a) building the two substances into a crystal, in which case the lattice forces will hold them together; (b) evaporating the solvent in which both substances are dissolved, so that the molecules will be in close proximity; (c) freezing the water solution of the mixture so that it will crystallize out and leave the molecules in intimate contact.

To test whether the photoreceptors exhibit properties of a solid state system, experiments have been carried out on the photoconductivity of carotenoids. Semiconduction and thermoluminescence studies indicate that there is a photoconductive mechanisms of energy transfer actively participating in the chloroplast (Arnold and Clayton, 1960). Experiments of Rosenberg *et al.* (1961) suggest that a sim-

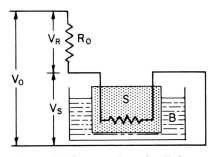

V_0 = known constant S.C.
voltage (10,000 cps)

R_0 = known constant resistance

S = sample (sealed in tube)

B = temperature bath

Figure 98 Construction of cell for measuring the conductance of rhodopsin.

ilar photoconductive mechanism with a semiconduction activation
energy of 2.3 e.v. is found for the retinal rods, which they suggest is
related to the photoisomerization of rhodopsin (the isomerization of
retinene from the all-trans to its active form the 11-cis; Wald, 1961b).
The photoconduction excitation spectrum was roughly determined
to correspond to absorption in the α and β bands of rhodopsin. The
major portion of the response is in the region of 420-550 mμ.

We have measured an activation energy for frog rhodopsin in
the experimental cell as shown in Figure 98. Rhodopsin which is
relatively stable to temperatures of 25°C. had an activation energy
of 0.45 e.v. (Fig. 99). Rhodopsin subjected to a constant dc potential carried an initial current which rapidly dropped off to a
much lower steady value, indicating polarization which set up a
reverse potential within the rhodopsin. This is not necessarily an
indication of further charge carriers (Ioffe, 1960). Ionic conduc-

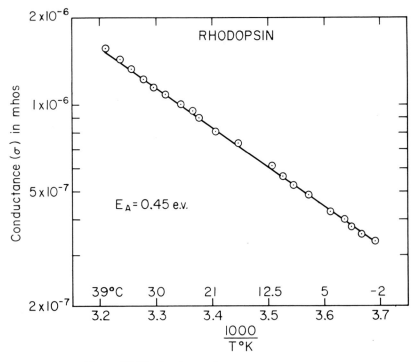

Figure 99 Rhodopsin conductance measurements.

tivity is indicated by the decrease in resistance to dc potential above 2 volts, and our observations could be due to ionic charge carriers.

Hagins and Jennings (1959) pointed out the need for a mechanism of energy migration in the system of retinal rods. They found the retinal rods to be free of all photodichroism, which suggests an efficient process of intermolecular, radiationless energy transfer. However, quite concentrated solutions of vitamin A, the prosthetic group of rhodopsin, show a strongly polarized fluorescence, indicating a relatively inefficient radiationless energy transfer process. The conclusion is that the photosensitizing action of rhodopsin must depend upon some other process of signal transmission such as photoconduction, electrolytic conduction, or molecular diffusion.

Chapter IX

SUMMARY

W̶E BEGAN WITH the hypothesis that the basis for visual excitation can be found at the molecular level. This hypothesis has been pursued through a phylogenetic comparative analysis of the structure and pigments of a variety of invertebrate and vertebrate eyes. We begin with protozoan eyespots and encompass the more complex photoreceptors of the flatworms, the arthropods, the molluscs, and the vertebrates, including those of man. The results of this survey are schematically illustrated in Figure 100. Some of the structural data are summarized in Table IX.

We therefore began to experiment with *Euglena,* a single celled protozoan flagellate with which we have tried to indicate how a primitive sensory system (eyespot + flagellum) can serve as an experimental model for study about higher levels of development. For *Euglena,* whose behavior is analogous to a photocell, movement is a light-searching process, which also bears a relation to the movement of the muscles of the eye in discriminating the form of different objects. This kind of muscular action is also found in the flatworms where the tendency to avoid light seems to be controlled by the balance of the impulses from its two eyes.

The flagellum (f), a sensory fiber associated with the eyespot of flagellates, is also found associated with sensory cells throughout all phyla. All flagella are similar in structure, including those fibrils that penetrate the outer through the inner segments of the vertebrate retinal rods and cones as in Figs. 33a and 60c.

Image forming, compound eyes are found in the arthropods (e.g., insects, arachnids, and crustacea) and in the molluscs (e.g., *Octopus* and *Squid*). They are of considerable interest in understanding the function of the visual apparatus. The compound eye is composed of numerous ommatidia, numbering only a few in the ant and as

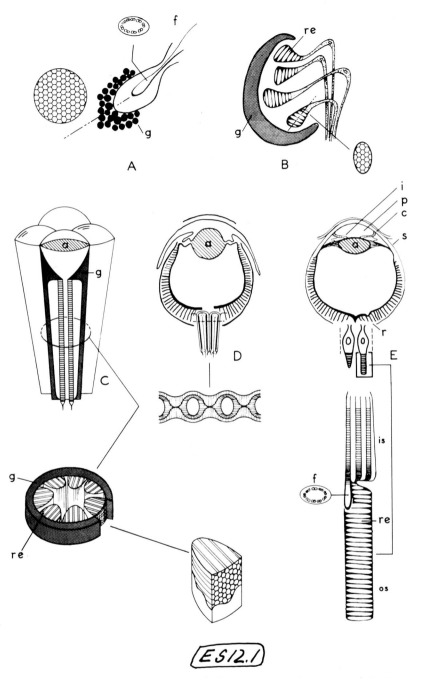

Figure 100. Structural development of photoreceptors. A, eyespot of *protozoa;* B, sensory cell of flatworm; C, compound eye of insects; D, mollusc cephalopod eye; and E, vertebrate eye. f, flagellum; g, pigment screening granules; re, vertebrate retinal rod structure; os, outer segment; and is, inner segment.

TABLE IX

VARIETY OF ANIMAL RETINAL PHOTORECEPTORS: AVERAGE MEASUREMENT

Animal	Photoreceptor	Diam. μ	Length μ	Volume cm³	Total Thickness of Layer Å	Kind of Packing
INVERTEBRATES						
Platyhelminth Planaria	Sensory cell (retinal rod)	5.0	35	6.9×10^{-10}	140	tubes
Arthropods *Drosophila melanogaster* (fruitfly)	Rhabdomere (retinal rod)	1.2	60	6.8×10^{-11}	120	,,
(housefly)	Rhabdomere (retinal rod)	1.2	60	6.8×10^{-11}	100	,,
Periplaneta americana (cockroach)	Rhabdomere (retinal rod)	2.0	100	3.1×10^{-10}	100	,,
Molluscs *Octopus vulgaris*	Rhabdomere (retinal rod)	1.0	60	4.7×10^{-11}	200	,,
Sepia officinalis (cuttlefish)	Rhabdomere (retinal rod)	1.0	60	4.7×10^{-11}	200	,,
VERTEBRATES						
Frog	Retinal rod outer segment	6.0	55	1.5×10^{-9}	150	plates
Perch	Retinal rod outer segment	1.5	40	6.2×10^{-11}	150	,,
Chicken	Retinal rod outer segment	3.5	35	3.4×10^{-11}	200	,,
Cattle	Retinal rod outer segment	1.0	10	7.5×10^{-12}	100	,,
Monkey	Retinal rod outer segment	1.3	22	2.3×10^{-11}	200	,,
Man	Retinal rod outer segment	1.0	28	1.6×10^{-10}	100	,,

(Modified from Wolken, 1961a). Each layer is considered to be a double layer in which each membrane is of the order of 50 Å in thickness.

many as a thousand in the dragonfly. Each ommatidium (Figs. 66 and 67) consists of retinula cells that form a rhabdome, the retina. Each retinula cell has a differentiated photoreceptor structure, a rhabdomere, which is believed to function in a manner similar to the vertebrate retinal rods.

Structurally, the rhabdomeres (retinal rods) are packed tubes from 300 to 500 Å in diameter, with walls of the order of 50 Å in thickness (Figs. 65 to 68). The rhabdomeres that form the rhabdome are of an *open* type as seen in the fruitfly (*Drosophila*, Fig. 66) or of a *closed* type as observed for the cockroach (Fig. 68).

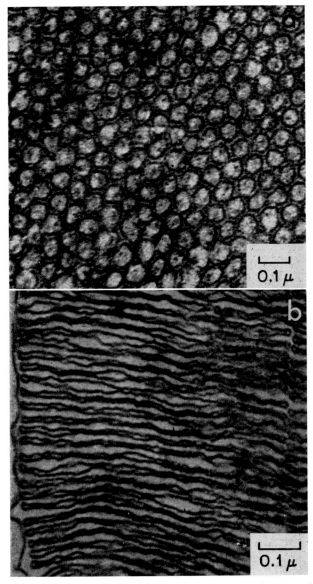

Figure 101a Cross-section of invertebrate photoreceptors showing the packed
tubules at high magnification; electron micrograph.

b. Section of vertebrate photoreceptors showing the lamellar structure
at high magnification; electron micrograph.

The closed or fused rhabdome as seen in the insects is also found in the crustacea (Figs. 71 and 72) and molluscs (Figs. 74 to 76) and even in the vertebrate retinal rod of amphibians (Fig. 32b). This may be one of the clues to the evolutionary development of the vertebrate retinal rod (compare Figs. 68, 71, 72 with Fig. 33). What function this fused structure gives to the retinal photoreceptors

CAROTENOIDS IN PHOTORECEPTOR SYSTEMS

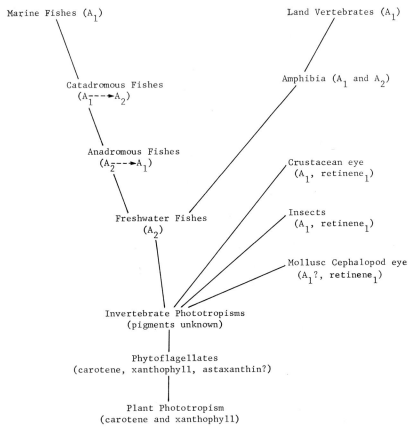

Figure 102 Carotenoids in photoreceptor systems (modified from G. Wald, 1952).

is not known; however, such a fused structure increases the surface area available for the visual pigments and hence for light capture (e.g., there are 10^9 rhodopsin molecules per frog rod and only 10^6 rhodopsin molecules per cattle rod).

In comparison to the invertebrates, all the vertebrate retinal rod and cone outer segments, as observed with the electron microscope, are stacked dense plates with a repeat unit of the order of 250 Å and separated by less dense interspaces. Each dense plate or disc is a double membraned structure with membranes of the order of 50 Å in thickness. These two types of structures, tubes for the invertebrates (Fig. 101a) and plates for the vertebrates (Fig. 101b), can be observed, depending on how one rolls up a membrane (a sheet) which can give either a tube-like or a plate-like geometric structure as illustrated schematically in Figure 94.

Not only do we have similarities in the pattern of molecular organization for all the photoreceptor structures, but, even more important, may be the fact that all of these photoreceptors depend on a single molecular group of pigments, the carotenoids (Fig. 102) for their function.

All visual pigments, thus far isolated, contain retinene (vitamin A aldehyde) as the prosthetic group; however, in vertebrate retinal rods, only the 11-cis (neo-b) geometric isomer complexes with—or is trapped by—the protein, opsin, to form rhodopsin.

Vitamin A and its aldehyde, retinene, are intimately related to the structure and function of the retinal rods and cones. A sequence of changes restricted to the visual cells is exhibited by animals when maintained on vitamin A acid, which sustains life but does not provide retinene for the retina. First, there is the decline in rhodopsin concentration, accompanied by a rise of visual threshold, followed by the disintegration of the rod outer segments. The failure to form visual pigments has specific anatomical consequences; the outer segments of the visual cells deteriorate, followed by the loss of almost all the retinal cells. The animal becomes blind and cannot recover its vision. These changes resemble those observed in certain hereditary forms of blindness and in human *retinitis pigmentosa*. These experiments indicate that the integrity of the organized retinal rod lamellar (membranes) structure is dependent upon the chemistry (the synthesis of the visual pigment retinene with opsin) and that this specific molecular arrangement stabilizes the molecular structure.

Retinene is a linear molecule of the order of 5 Å in diameter with a molecular weight of the order 280. When combined with opsin to form rhodopsin, it would be of the order of 50 Å in diameter if a globular molecule. The rhodopsin molecules could easily lie in or on the membrane as depicted in our model (see Fig. 89). Its molecular weight would depend on the protein, opsin, the exact chemical nature of which is not known but which appears to be species-specific. The molecular weights for rhodopsins that have been determined are in the range of 30,000 to 60,000.

One of the most interesting and useful extractants for obtaining vertebrate rhodopsin from the retinal rods is 2 per cent aqueous digitonin solution. Rhodopsins extracted by this method exhibit in solution photochemical activity (light $<--->$ dark reactions) similar to the *in situ* retinal rod. Digitonin in solution forms colloid aggregates, micelles, of the order of 75,000 to 225,000 molecular weight which have a dye-binding capacity for carotenoids. The digitonin micelles may behave like an enzyme, simultaneously reacting with one of the substrates (retinene) and attracting the other substrate (opsin) to the same vicinity (Figs. 89 and 96). Opsin specifically traps retinene when in the right molecular configuration. The retinene, protein, and lipids in the micelles are in the same relative concentration as in the intact retinal rod; therefore the rhodopsin molecule becomes aligned in these structures as visualized in our schematic molecular model for the retinal rod (Fig. 89).

Color vision is one of the most interesting of the visual phenomena. It is not yet completely understood, but it is known that color vision is associated with the photosensitive cone pigments; however, by extraction procedures, only one cone pigment has been isolated: either iodopsin (retinene$_1$) 562 mμ, or cyanopsin (retinene$_2$) 620 mμ (Figs. 16 and 17). Recent spectral studies done by microspectrophotometry on single cones have indicated that at least three different absorption peaks are found for the cones: a blue-sensitivity about 445 mμ; a green-sensitivity about 540 mμ; and a red-sensitivity beyond 560 mμ. Even additional absorption peaks cannot be ruled out. These spectral studies on individual cones are now

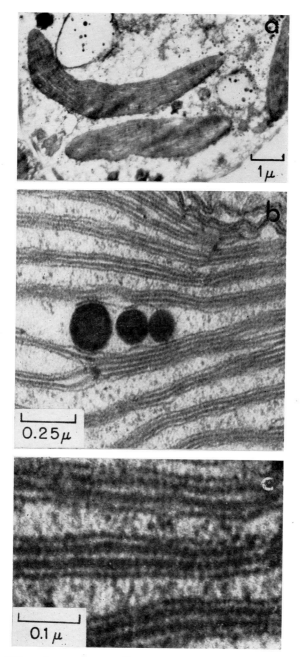

Figure 103 Chloroplast structure. *Euglena gracilis*. a. cross-section;
b. higher magnification of chloroplast section showing the lamellae;
c. high resolution showing the globules (50 - 150 Å in diameter) of the
chloroplast lamellae. Note similarities to globules in lamellae of human retinal rod in Fig. 93.

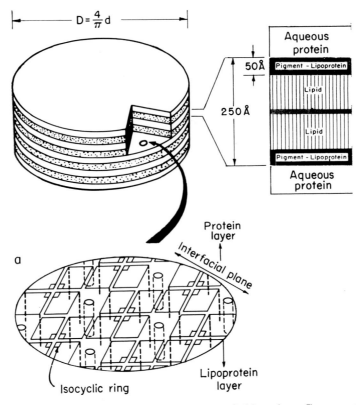

Figure 103d. Schematic molecular arrangement of chloroplast. Compare to molecular model for the retinal rod Fig. 89.

beginning to fit into place with the spectral sensitivity data on the living eye and with the psychophysical tri-color theories for color vision proposed a century ago.

Closely associated with the retinal cones of amphibians, reptiles, and birds, are red, yellow, and green oil globules. The absorption spectra for globules from a variety of animals suggests that they contain a mixture of carotenoids, but that only one carotenoid predominates in each globule. It is implied that the globules can function in color vision, since the shapes of the absorption curves for each colored globule indicate that they can act as bandpass color filters (Figs. 45, 47, and 48).

All photoreceptors are energy transferring devices, transducers i.e.,

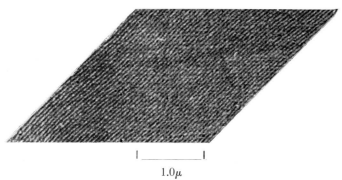

1.0μ

Figure 104 Photoreceptor area showing the crystalline-structure
of a photoreceptor.

they convert light energy to chemical and to electrical energy, which
initiate the processes of photosythesis and vision. This molecular
organization for the visual photoreceptors then is not unique to
visual cells for the utilization of light energy. It has counterparts
in the plastids of algae and the chloroplasts of higher plants in the
process of photosynthesis (Fig. 103).

As we approach molecular dimensions for all photoreceptors, there
is a basic pattern of organization. This structure has similarities to
the lattice structure of crystals (Fig. 104), a concept which has led
to the idea that photoreceptors may bear a close relation to the physics
of the solid state. Here lies a clue to the function of energy transferring systems in the living state. The interpolation of this highly
ordered crystalline structure of the retinal photoreceptors, then,
must be that it can provide for the orientation of the photosensitive
visual pigments; hence it is an efficiency mechanism for light capture. Its structure may also be necessary for function, that is, for the
initiation of the visual process.

REFERENCES

Ackerman, E.: *Biophysical Science*. Englewood, New Jersey, Prentice-Hall, 1962, p. 489.

Albrecht, G.: Terminal amino acids of rhodopsin. *J. Biol. Chem.*, *229*:477, 1957.

Arden, G.B.: Light-sensitive pigments in the visual cells of the frog. *J. Physiol.*, *123*:377, 1954.

Arens, J.F., and van Dorp, D.A.: Synthesis of some compounds possessing vitamin A activity. *Nature, 157*:190, 1946.

Arnold, W., and Clayton, R.C.: The first step in photosynthesis: evidence for its electronic nature. *Proc. Nat. Acad. Sc., 46*:769, 1960.

Autrum, H.: Die belechtungs potentiale und das sehen der insekten (untersuching an *Calliphora* und *Dixippus*). *Z. Vergleich. Physiol., 32*:176, 1950.

Autrum, H.: Electrophysiological analysis of the visual systems in insects. *Exp. Cell Res.,* Suppl. 5, p. 426, 1958.

Autrum, H., and Stumpf, H.: Das bienenaugen als analystor fur polarisiertes licht. *Z. Naturforsch., 56*:116, 1950.

Ball, S., Collins, F.D., Dalvi, P.D., and Morton, R.A.: Studies in vitamin A. II. Reactions of retinene$_1$ with amino compounds. *Biochem. J., 45*:304, 1949.

Ball, S., Goodwin, T.W., and Morton, R.A.: Studies in vitamin A. 5. The preparation of retinene$_1$—vitamin A aldehyde. *Biochem. J., 42*:516, 1948.

Beaven, G.H., and Holiday, E.R.: Ultraviolet absorption spectra of proteins and amino acids. *Adv. Protein Chem., 7*:319, 1952.

Blatz, P.E.: The Role of Carbonium Ions in Color Reception. *J. Gen. Physiol., 48*:753, 1965.

Bliss, A.F.: The absorption spectra of visual purple of the squid and its bleaching products. *J. Biol. Chem., 176*:563, 1948.

Böll, F.: *Zur Anatomie und Physiologie der Retina*. Monatsber. preuss, Akad. Wiss., Berlin, 1876, p. 783.

Bowness, J.M., and Wolken, J.J.: A light-sensitive yellow pigment from the housefly. *J. Gen. Physiol., 42*:779, 1959.

Bowness, J.M.: Preparation of rhodopsin using columns containing calcium triphosphate. *Biochim. et Biophys. Acta, 31*:305, 1959.

Broda, E.E.: The role of the phospholipid in visual purple solutions. *J. Biochem., 35*:960, 1941.

Brode, W.R.: *Chemical Spectroscopy.* New York, John Wiley and Sons Inc., 1943.

Brown, P.K.: A system for microspectrophotometry employing a commerical recording spectrophotometer. *J. Optic. Soc. America, 51*:1000, 1961.

Brown, P.K., and Brown, P.S.: Visual pigments of the octopus and cuttlefish. *Nature, 182*:1288, 1958.

Brown, P.K., and Wald, G.: Visual Pigments in Single Rods and Cones of the human retina. *Science, 144*:45, 1964.

Brown, P.K., and Wald, G.: Visual pigments in human and monkey retinas. *Nature, 200*:37, 1963.

Buriain, H.M., and Ziv, B.: Electric response of the phakic and aphakic human eye to stimulation with near ultraviolet. *Arch. Ophth., 61*:347, 1959.

Butenandt, A.: The mode of action of hereditary factors. *Endeavor, 11*:188, 1952.

Butenandt, A., Schiedt, V., and Biekert, E.: Uber ommochrome. III. Mitteilung synthese des zanthommatins. *Ann. Chem. Justus Liebigs, 588*:106, 1954.

Caspersson, T.O.: Quantitative cytochemistry for the study of normal and abnormal growth. *Fed. Proc. 20*:858, 1961.

Caspersson, T.O.: *Cell Growth and Cell Function.* New York, Norton, 1950.

Caspersson, T.O., Lomakka, G.M., Svensson, G., and Säfström, R.: A versatile ultramicrospectrograph for multiple line surface scanning high resolution measurements employing automatized data analysis. *Exp. Cell Res.,* Suppl. 3, p. 30, 1955.

Caspersson, T.O., and Lomakka, G.M.: Scanning microscopy techniques for high resolution quantitative cytochemistry. *Ann. N.Y. Acad. Sc., 97*:449, 1962.

Chance, B.: Fluorescence emission of mitochondrial DPNH as a factor in the ultraviolet sensitivity of visual receptors. *Proc. Nat. Acad. Sc., 51*:359, 1964.

Chance, B., and Baltscheffsky, J.: Respiratory enzymes in oxidative phosphorylation. *J. Biol. Chem., 233*:736, 1958.

Chance, B., and Jöbsis, F.F.: Changes in fluorescence in a frog sartorius muscle following a twitch. *Nature, 184*:195, 1959.

Chance, B., Perry, R., Akerman, L., and Thorell, B.: Highly sensitive recording microspectrophotometer. *Rev. Sci. Instr., 30*:735, 1959.

Cohen, A.I.: Some observations on the fine structure of the retinal receptors of the American gray squirrel. *Invest. Ophthal., 3*:198, 1964.

Cohen, A.I.: Vertebrate retinal cells and their organization. *Biol. Rev. Cambridge Philos. Soc., 38*:427, 1963a.

Cohen, A.I.: The fine structure of the visual receptors of the pigeon. *Exp. Eye Res., 2*:88, 1963b.

Cohen, A.I.: The fine structure of the extra-foveal receptors of the Rhesus monkey. *Exp. Eye Res., 1*:128, 1961.

Collins, F.D.: Chemistry of vision. *Biol. Rev. Cambridge Philos. Soc., 29*:453, 1954.

Collins, F.D., Love, R.M., and Morton, R.A.: Studies on rhodopsin. 4. Preparation of rhodopsin, *Biochem. J., 51*:292, 1952.

Dartnall, H.J.A.: *The Visual Pigments.* New York, John Wiley and Sons, Inc., 1957.

Dartnall, H.J.A.: Photobiology of the visual process. In *The Eye,* Hugh Davson, ed., New York, Academic Press, 1962, Vol. II, 323-469.

Denton, E.J.: The contributions of the orientated photosensitive and other molecules to the absorption of whole retina. *Proc. Roy. Soc., London, S.B., 150*:78, 1959.

Denton, E.J., and Wyllie, J.H.: Study of the photosensitive pigments in the pink and green rods of the frog. *J. Physiol., 127*:81, 1955.

De Robertis, E.: Electron microscope observations on the submicroscopic organization of retinal rods. *J. Biophys. Biochem. Cytol., 2*:319, 1956.

De Robertis, E. and Lassansky, A.: Ultrastructure and chemical organization of photoreceptors. In *The Structure of the Eye,* G.K. Smelser, ed., New York, Academic Press, 1961, p. 29.

Dietrich, W.: Die facettenaugen der dipteran. *Z. wissensch. zool., 92*:465, 1909.

Dodt, E., and Walther, J.B.: Fluorescence of the crystalline lens and electroretinographic sensitivity determinations. *Nature, 181*:286, 1958.

Donnell, von R., and Zeutschel, B.: Uber der feinbau der retinula bei *Drosophila melanogaster. Z. Naturforsch., 12b*:581, 1957.

Donner, K.O.: *Coloquio sobre problemas opticas de la vision* (Madrid) *2*:1, 1953.

Donner, K.O.: The spectral sensitivity of the pigeon's retinal elements. *J. Physiol., 122*:524, 1950.

van Dorp, D.A., and Arens, J.F.: Synthesis of vitamin A aldehyde. *Nature, 160*:189, 1947.

van Dorp, D.A. and Arens, J.F.: Synthesis of vitamin A acid bioactive substance, *Rec. Traz. Chim. Pays-Bas, 65*:338, 1946.

Dowling, J.E.: Foveal receptors of the monkey retina; Fine structure, *Science, 147*, 57, 1965.

Dowling, J.E., and Wald, G.: The biological function of vitamin A acid. *Proc. Nat. Acad. Sc., 46*:587, 1960.

Duke-Elder, Sir Stewart: *System of Ophthalmology. The Eye in Evolution*, St. Louis, C.V. Mosby, Co., 1958, Vol. I.

Ephrussi, B., and Herold, J.L.: Studies of eye pigments of *Drosophila*. I. Methods of extraction and quantitative estimation of pigment components. *Genetics, 29*:148, 1944.

Exner, S.: *Die Physiologie der Facettierten Augen von Krebsen und Insekten*. Liepzig, Germany, 1891.

Fernández-Morán, H.: The fine structure of vertebrate and invertebrate photoreceptors as revealed by low-temperature electron microscopy. In *The Structure of the Eye*, G.K. Smelser, ed., New York, Academic Press, 1961, p. 521.

Fernández-Morán, H.: Low temperature preparation techniques for electron microscopy of biological specimens based on rapid freezing. *Ann. N.Y. Acad. Sc., 85*:869, 1960.

Fernández-Morán, H.: Fine structure of biological lamellar systems. *Revs. Mod. Phys., 31*:2, 319, 1959.

Fernández-Morán, H.: Fine structure of the light receptor in the eyes of insects. *Exp. Cell Res., 5*:586, 1958.

Fernández-Morán, H.: Fine structure of the insect retinula as revealed by electron microscopy. *Nature, 177*:742, 1956.

Fernández-Morán, H., and Brown, R.: The submicroscopic organization and function of nerve cells. *Exp. Cell Res.*, Suppl. 5, 1958.

Fingerman, M.: The role of the eye pigments of *Drosophila melanogaster* in photic orientation. *J. Exp. Zool., 120*:131, 1952.

Fingerman, M., and Brown, F.A.: Color discrimination and physiological duplicity of *Drosophila* vision. *Physiol. Zool., 26*:59, 1953.

Fingerman, M., and Brown, F.A.: A "Purkinje Shift" in insect vision. *Science, 116*:171, 1952.

Forrest, H.S., and Mitchell, H.K.: *The Pteridines of Drosophila Melanogaster, In Chemistry and Biology of Pteridines*, Ciba Foundation Symposium, Boston, Little, Brown, and Co., 1954a, p. 143.

Forrest, H.S., and Mitchell, H.K.: Pteridines from *Drosophila*. I. Isolation of a yellow pigment. *J. Am. Chem. Soc., 76*:5688, 1954b.

Fox, D.L.: *Animal Biochromes and Structural Colors.* Cambridge, Cambridge University Press, 1953, p. 63-190.

Frisch, K. von: Geloste und ungeloste rätsel der bienensprache. *Naturwiss., 35*:38, 1948.

Frisch, K. von: *Bees. Their Vision, Chemical Senses and Language.* Ithaca, Cornell University Press, 1950.

Frisch, K. von: *The Dancing Bees.* New York, Harcourt, Brace, and Co., 1953.

Fujimoto, K., Yanase, T., and Hanaoka, T.: Spectral transmittance of retinal colored oil globules re-examined with microspectrophotometer. *Jap. J. Physiol., 7*:339, 1957.

Garten, S.: Die veränderungen der netzhaut durch licht. In *Handb. d. ges. Augenh.,* Vol. 3, 1907.

Geiger, R. S.: Subcultures of adult mammalian brain cortex *in vitro. Exp. Cell Res., 14*:541, 1958.

Geiger, R.S.: Ultrastructure and cellular chemistry of neural tissue. In *Progress in Neurobiology.* H. Walsh, ed., London, Cassell and Co., Ltd., 1957, p. 83.

Giliam, A.E.: Spectrometric measurements on various carotenoids. *Biochem. J., 29*:1831, 1935.

Glees, P.: *Neuroglia, Morphology, and Function.* Springfield, Thomas, 1955.

Glover, J., Goodwin, T.W., and Morton, R.A.: Conversion *in vivo* of vitamin A aldehyde (retinene$_1$) to vitamin A$_1$. *Biochem. J., 43*:109, 1948.

Goldsmith, T.H.: The physiological basis of wavelength discrimination in the eye of the honeybee. In *Sensory Communications,* W.A. Rosenblith, ed., New York, John Wiley and Sons Inc., 1961, p. 357.

Goldsmith, T.H.: The visual system of the honeybee. *Proc. Nat. Acad. Sc., 44*:123, 1958a.

Goldsmith, T.H.: On the visual system of the bee *(Apis Mellifera). Ann. N. Y. Acad. Sc., 74*:223, 1958b.

Goldsmith, T.H., Barker, R.J., and Cohen, C.F.: Sensitivity of visual receptors of carotenoid-depleted flies: A vitamin A deficiency in an invertebrate. *Science, 146*:65, 1964.

Goldsmith, T.H., and Philpott, D.E.: The microstructure of the compound eyes of insects. *J. Biophys. Biochem. Cytol., 3*:429, 1957.

Goldsmith, T.H., and Ruck, P.R.: The spectral sensitivities of the dorsal ocelli of cockroaches and honeybees. *J. Gen. Physiol., 41*:1171, 1958.

Goldsmith, T.H., and Warner, L.T.: Vitamin A in the vision of insects, *J. Gen Physiol., 47*:433, 1964.

Goodwin, T.W.: *Comparative Biochemistry of Carotenoids,* London, Chapman and Hall, Ltd., 1952.

Goodwin, T.W., and Jamikorn, M.: Studies in carotenogenesis. Some observations on carotenoid synthesis in two varieties of *Euglena. J. Protozool., 1*:216, 1954.

Granit, R.: *Receptors and Sensory Perception.* New Haven, Yale University Press, 1955.

Granit, R.: Colour receptors of the frog's retina. *Acta. Physiol. Scandinav., 3*:137, 1941.

Gregory, R.L., Ross, H.E., and Moray, N.: The curious eye of *Copilia, Nature, 201*:1166, 1964.

Grenacher, H.: Abhandlugen zur vergleichenden anatomie des auges. I. Die retina der cephalopoden. *Naturforsch. Ges. Hall. Abhandl., 16*:207, 1883-1886.

Hagins, W.A., and Jennings, W.H.: Radiationless migration of electronic excitation in retinal rods. *Disc. Faraday Soc., 27*:180, 1959.

Hanaoka, T., and Fujimoto, K.: Absorption spectrum of a single cone in the carp retina. *Jap. J. Physiol., 7*:276, 1957.

Hawkins, E.G.E., and Hunter, R.F.: Vitamin A aldehyde. *J. Chem. Soc., 411*:1944.

Hedges, E.: *Liesegang Rings and Other Periodic Structures.* London, Chapman and Hall, Ltd., 1932.

Helmholtz, H. von: *Handbuch der Physiologischen Optik.* Leipzig, Leopold Voss, 1867, p. 874.

Helmholtz, H. von: Uber die theorie der zusammemgesetzien farben. *Ann. Physik., 87*:45, 1852.

Henry, B., and Cole.H.: Single crystal CdSe as soft x-ray detector. *Rev. Sci. Instr., 30*:90, 1959.

Hering, E.: *Ueber Individual Veischiedenheiten des Farbensinnes.* Prague, Lotos, 1885.

Hering, E.: Grundzüge der lehre von lichtsinn. *Handb. ges. Augen Heilk.* Graef-Saemisch, Springer, Berlin, 1925, Vol. III, pt. XII, pp. 1-294.

Hering, E.: *Outlines of a Theory of the Light Sense,* L.M. Hurvich and D. Jameson, trans. Cambridge, Harvard University Press, 1965.

Hess, W.N.: Visual organs of invertebrate animals. *Scientific Monthly, 57*:489, 1943.

Heyden, H.: The neuron. In *The Cell,* J. Brachet and A.E. Mirsky, eds., New York, Academic Press, 1960, Vol. 4, p. 215.

Hild, W., and Tasaki, I.: Morphological and physiological properties of neurons and glial cells in tissue culture. *J. Neurophysiol., 25*:277, 1962.

Hill, R., and Bendall, F.: Function of the two cytochrome components in chloroplasts: A working hypothesis. *Nature, 186*:136, 1960.

Hubbard, R.: The molecular weight of rhodopsin and the nature of the rhodopsin-digitonin complex. *J. Gen. Physiol., 37*:381, 1954.

Hubbard, R., and Kropf, A.: Chicken lumi- and meta-rhodopsin, *Nature, 183*:448, 1959a.

Hubbard, R., and Kropf, A.: Molecular aspects of visual excitation. *Ann. N. Y. Acad. Sc., 81*:388, 1959b.

Hubbard, R., Brown, P.K., and Kropf, A.: Action of light on the visual pigments. *Nature, 183*:442, 1959.

Hubbard, R., Gregerman, R.I., and Wald, G.: Geometrical isomers of retinene. *J. Gen. Physiol., 36*:415, 1953.

Hubbard, R., and St. George, R.C.C.: The rhodopsin system of the *squid. J. Gen. Physiol., 41*:501, 1958.

Hubbard, R., and Wald, G.: Visual pigment of the horseshoe crab, *Limulus polyphemus. Nature, 186*:212, 1960.

Hunter, R.F., and Williams, N.E.: Chemical conversion of β-carotene into vitamin A. *J. Chem. Soc., 554,* 1945.

Ioffe, A.F.: *Physics of Semiconductors,* New York, Academic Press, 1960.

Jörschke, H.: Die facettenaugen der orthopteren und termiten. *Z. wissensch. Zool., 111*:153, 1914.

Kampa, E.M.: Euphausiopsin. A new photosensitive pigment from the eyes of euphausiid crustaceans. *Nature, 175*:996, 1955.

Karrer, P., and Jucker, E.: *Carotenoids.* Rev. by E.A. Braude, Amsterdam, Elsevier Press, Inc., 1950.

Kay, Desmond: *Techniques for Electron Microscopy.* Oxford, England, Blackwell Scientific Publishers, 1963.

Kennedy, D.: Physiology of photoreceptor neurons in the abdominal nerve cord of the crayfish, *J. Gen. Physiol., 46*:551, 1963.

Kikkawa, H.: Mechanism of pigment formation in *Bombyx* and *Drosophila. Genetics, 26*:587, 1941.

Kikkawa, H., Ogita, Z., and Fujito, S.: Nature of pigments derived from tyrosine and tryptophan in animals. *Science, 121*:43, 1955.

Krinsky, N.I., and Goldsmith, T.H.: The carotenoids of the flagellated alga, *Euglena gracilis. Arch. Biochem. Biophys., 91*:271, 1960.

Kühne, W.: Zur photochemie der netzhaut. *Untersuchungen Physiol. Inst. Univ. Heidelberg, 1* : 1, 1877.

Kühne, W.: Uber den sehpurpurs. *Untersuchungen Physiol. Inst. Univ. Heidelberg, 1* : 15, 1877.

Kühne, W.: Das sehen ohne sehpurpur. *Untersuchungen Physiol. Inst. Univ. Heidelberg, 1* : 119, 1877.

Kuiper, J. W.: The optics of the compound eye. In *Biological Receptor Mechanisms*. J.W.L. Beament, ed., New York, Academic Press, 1962, p. 58.

Lassansky, A.: Morphological bases for a missing role of glia in the toad retina. Electron microscope observations. *J. Biophys. Biochem. Cytol., 11* : 237, 1961.

Last, R.J.: *Wolff's Anatomy of the Eye and Orbit*. 5th Ed., Philadelphia, W.B. Saunders, 1961.

Lecomte de Noüy, P.: *Surface Equilibria of Biological and Organic Colloids*. New York, The Chemical Catalogue Co., 1926.

Liebman, P.A.: *In situ* microspectrophotometric studies on the pigments of single retinal rods. *Biophys. J., 2* : 161, 1962.

Liebman, P.A. and Entine, G.: Sensitive low-light level of microspectrophotometric detection of photosensitive pigment of retinal cones. *J. Optic. Soc. Am., 54* : 1451, 1964.

Liss, L., and Wolter, J.R.: Human retinal neurons in tissue culture. *Am. J. Ophthal., 52* : 834, 1961.

Lowe, M.B., and Phillips, J.N.: Catalysis of metalloporphyrin formation: A possible enzyme model for haem iron incorporation. *Nature, 190* : 262, 1961.

Lumiérè, A.M.L., in E. Wallon: *Bulletin de la Societe Francaise de Photographie, 8* : 225, 1921.

MacNichol, E.F.: Three pigment color vision, *Scientific American, 211* : 48, 1964.

Manten, A.: Phototaxis, phototropism and photosynthesis in purple bacteria and blue-green algae. Thesis, Drukkirij Fa. Schotanus and Jens. Utrecht, Holland, 1948.

Marak, G.E., and Wolken, J.J.: An action spectrum for the fire ant. *(Solenopsis Saevissima) Nature, 205* : 1328, 1965.

Marks, W.B., Dobelle, W.H., and MacNichol, J.R.: Visual pigments of single primate cones. *Science, 143* : 1181, 1964.

Marks, W.B.: *Difference spectra of the visual pigments in single goldfish cones*. Thesis, Johns Hopkins University, Baltimore, Maryland, 1963.

Maturana, H.R., Lettvin, J.Y., McCulloch, W.S. and Pitts, W.H.,

Anatomy and physiology of vision in the frog *(Rana pipiens)*, *J. Gen. Physiol.*, *43*:pt. 2, 129, 1960.

Maxwell, J.C.: On the theory of compound colours and the relations of the colours of the spectrum. *Phil. Tr. Roy. Soc. London, 150*:57, 1861.

Maxwell, J.C.: On the theory of compound colours and the relations of the colours of the spectrum. *Scientific Papers*, Cambridge, 1890, Vol. I, p. 410.

McConnell, D.G., and Scarpelli, D.G.: Rhodopsin: An enzyme. *Science, 138*:848, 1963.

Miller, W.H.: Fine structure of some invertebrate photoreceptors. *Ann. N. Y. Acad. Sc., 74*:204, 1958.

Miller, W.H.: Morphology of the ommatidia of the compound eye of *Limulus. J. Biophys. Biochem. Cytol., 3*:421, 1957.

Miller, W.H.: Visual photoreceptor structures. In *The Cell.* J. Brachet and A.E. Mirsky, eds., New York, Academic Press, 1960, Vol. IV, p. 1.

Missotten, L., L'ultrastructure des tissues oculaire, *Bull. de la Société Belge d'ophthalmologie, 135*:1, 1964.

Molyneux, W.: *Dioptrica nova.* 2nd Ed., London, printed for B. Tooke, 1709.

Morgan, J.F., Morten, H.J., and Parker, R.C.: Nutrition of animal cells in tissue culture. I. Initial studies on a synthetic medium. *Proc. Soc. Exper. Biol. Med., 73*:1, 1950.

Moore, T.: Vitamin A in the normal individual. In *Symposium on Nutrition,* R.M. Herriott, ed., Baltimore, Johns Hopkins University Press, 1953, p. 28.

Moore, T.: *Vitamin A.* New York, Elsevier Publishing Co., 1957.

Moorefield, H.: Improved method of harvesting housefly heads for use in cholinesterase studies. *Contrib. Boyce Thompson Inst., 18*:463, 1957.

Montgomery, P. O'B., ed.: Scanning Techniques in Biology and Medicine, *Ann. N. Y. Acad. Sc., 97*:331, 1962.

Morton, R.A.: Chemical aspects of the visual process. *Nature, 153*:69, 1944.

Morton, R.A., and Goodwin, T.W.: Preparation of retinene *in vitro. Nature, 153*:405, 1944.

Morton, R.A., Salah, M.K., and Stubbs, A.L.: Retinene$_2$-vitamin A$_2$ aldehyde, *Biochem. J., 40*:49, 1946.

Morton, R.A., Salah, M.K., and Stubbs, A.L.: Conversion of retinene$_2$ to vitamin A$_2$ *in vivo. Biochem. J., 41*:24, 1947.

Morton, R.A., and Collins, F.D.: I. Studies on rhodopsin. Methods of extraction and the absorption spectrum, *Biochem. J., 47*:3, 1950a.

Morton, R.A., and Collins, F.D.: Studies on rhodopsin. 2. Indicator yellow. *Biochem. J., 47*:10, 1950b.

Morton, R.A., and Collins, F.D.: Studies on rhodopsin. 3. Rhodopsin and transient orange. *Biochem. J., 47*:18, 1950c.

Morton, R.A., and Pitt, G.A.J.: Studies on rhodopsin. 9. pH and the hydrolysis of indicator yellow. *Biochem. J., 59*:128, 1955.

Naka, K.I.: Recording of Retinal Action Potentials from Single Cells in the Insect Compound Eye, *J. Gen. Physiol., 44*:571, 1960.

Nolte, D.S.: The eye pigmentary system of *Drosophila*. I. The pigment cells, *J. Genetics, 50*:79, 1950.

Nowikoff, M.: Ueber der bau der komplexaugen von *Periplaneta (Stylopyga) Orientalis, Jena Z. F. Naturwissensch., 67*:58, 1932.

Patten, W.: Eyes of molluscs and arthropods. *J. Morphol., 1*:67, 1887.

Pease, D.C.: *Histological Techniques for Electron Microscopy*, 2nd Ed. New York, Academic Press, 1964.

Pirenne, M.H., and Marriot, F.H.C.: Light sensitivity of the aquatic flatworm *Dendrocoelum lacteum. Nature, 175*:642, 1955.

Platt, J.R.: Carotene donor acceptor complexes in photosynthesis. *Science, 129*:372, 1959.

Pollister, A.W., and Ornstein, L.: The photometric chemical analysis. In *Analytical Cytology*. 2nd ed., R.C. Mellors, ed., McGraw-Hill, New York, 1959, p. 431.

Polyak, S.: *The Vertebrate Visual System*. Rev. Heinrich Klüver, ed., Chicago, University of Chicago Press, 1957.

Purkinje, J.: *Beobachtungen und versuche zur physiologie der sinne.* Vol. 2, G. Reimer, Berlin, 1825.

Rabinowitch, E.I.: *Photosynthesis,* New York, Interscience Publishers, Inc., 1951, Vol. II, Art. 1, p. 798.

Ramsey, J.A.: *A Physiological Approach to Lower Animals.* Cambridge, Cambridge University Press, 1952, p. 82.

Robinson, C., and Ward, J.C.: Liquid-crystalline structures in polypeptides. *Nature, 180*:1183, 1957.

Rölich, P., and Török, L.H.: Electronenmikroscopische untersuchunger des auges von planarien. *Z. Zellforsch. u. mikroskop. Anat., 54*:362, 1961.

Rosenberg, B.: Photoconductivity and the visual receptor process. *J. Opt. Soc. Am., 48*:581, 1958.

Rosenberg, B., Orlando, R.A., and Orlando, J.M.: Photoconduction and semiconduction in dried receptors of sheep eyes. *Arch. Biochem.,* *93*:395, 1961.

Rushton, W.A.H.: *The Visual Pigments in Man.* Liverpool, England, Liverpool University Press, 1962.

Rushton, W.A.H.: The kinetics of cone pigments measured objectively upon the living human fovea. *Ann. N.Y. Acad. Sc., 74*:291, 1958.

Rushton, W.A.H.: Electric records from the vertebrate optic nerve, *Brit. Med. Bull., 9*:68, 1953.

Saito, Z.: Isolierung der stäbchenaussenglieder und spektrale untersuchung der daraus hergesteuten sehpurpextraktes. *Tokohu J. Exp. Med., 32*:432, 1938.

Salah, M.K., and Morton, R.A.: Crystalline retinene$_2$. *Biochem. J., 43*:6, 1948.

Schmidt, W.J.: Polarisationsoptische analyse eines eiweiss-lipoid-systems erläutert am aussenglied der sehzellen'. *Kolloidzschr., 85*:137, 1938.

Schmidt, W.J.: *Die Doppelbrechung von Karoplasma, Zytoplasma, und Metaplasma, Protoplasma.* Berlin, Barntraeger, Monogr. II, 1937.

Schmidt, W.J.: Doppelbrechung, dichroismus und feinbau der aussenbliedes der sehzellen vom frosch. *Z. Zellforsch. u. mikroskop. Anat., 22*:485, 1935.

Schultz, M.: Zur anatomie und physiologie der retina. *Arch. Mikroskop. Anat., 2*:175, 1866.

Sidman, R.L.: The structure and concentration of solids in photoreceptor cells studied by refractometry and interference microscopy. *J. Biophys. Biochem. Cytol., 3*:15, 1957.

Siegel, B.M., ed., *Modern Developments in Electron Microscopy,* New York, Academic Press, 1964.

Sjöstrand, F.S.: Electron microscopy of the retina. In *The Structure of the Eye,* G.K. Smelser, ed., New York, Academic Press, 1961, p. 1.

Sjöstrand, F.S.: Morphology of ordered biological structures. In *Radiation Research, Bioenergetics.* L.G. Augustine, ed., New York, Academic Press, 1960, Supplement 2, p. 349.

Sjöstrand, F.S.: Fine structure of cytoplasm: The organization of membranous layers, *Revs. Mod. Phys., 31*:2, 301, 1959.

Sjöstrand, F.S.: The ultrastructure of the outer segments of rods and cones of the eye as revealed by the electron microscope. *J. Cell. Comp. Physiol., 42*:15, 1953a.

Sjöstrand, F.S.: The ultrastructure of the inner segments of the retinal rods of the guinea pig as revealed by the electron microscope. *J. Cell. Comp. Physiol., 42*:45, 1953b.

Sjöstrand, F.S.: An electron microscope study of the retinal rods of the guinea pig eye. *J. Cell. Comp. Physiol., 33*:383, 1949.

Stephens, G.C., Fingerman, M., and Brown, F.A.: The orientation of *Drosophila* to plane polarized light. *Ann. Entomol. Soc. Am., 46*:75, 1953.

Stern, K.H.: The liesegang phenomenon, *Chem. Revs. 54*:79, 1954.

St. George, R.C.C., and Wald, G.: The photosensitive pigment of the *squid* retina. *Biol. Bull. Woods Hole, 97*:248, 1949.

Strain, H.H.: Chloroplast pigments. *Ann. Rev. Biochem., 13*:591, 1944.

Strain, H.H.: *Chronica Botanica.* In *Manual of Phycology.* Waltham, Massachusetts, 1951, p. 243.

Strother, G.K.: Absorption spectra of retinal oil globules in turkey, turtle, and pigeon. *Exp. Cell Res., 29*:349, 1963.

Strother, G.K., and Wolken, J.J.: *In vivo* absorption spectra of *Euglena:* Chloroplast and eyespot. *J. Protozool., 8*:3, 261, 1961.

Strother, G.K., and Wolken, J.J.: Microspectrophotometry. I. Absorption spectra of colored oil globules in the chicken retina. *Exp. Cell Res., 21*:504, 1960a.

Strother, G.K., and Wolken, J.J.: Microspectrophotometry of *Euglena* chloroplast and eyespot. *Nature, 188*:601, 1960b.

Strother, G.K., and Wolken, J.J.: A simplified microspectrophotometer. *Science, 130*:1084, 1959.

Swift, H., and Rasch, E.: Microspectrophotometry with visible light. In *Physical Techniques in Biological Research.* G. Oster and A.W. Pollister, eds., New York, Academic Press, 1956, Vol. III, p. 353.

Tiselius, A.: Chromatography of proteins on calcium phosphate columns. *Arkiv. Kimi., 7*:443, 1954.

Vinnikov, J.A.: Transformation of the retinal ganglionic cells in tissue culture. *Nature, 158*:377, 1946.

Wald, G.: The receptors of human color. *Science, 145*:1007, 1964.

Wald, G.: General discussion of retinal structure in relation to the visual process. In *The Structure of the Eye.* G.K. Smelser, ed., New York, Academic Press, 1961a, p. 101.

Wald, G., The molecular organization of visual systems. In *Light and Life,* W.D. McElroy and B. Glass, eds., Johns Hopkins University Press, Baltimore, Maryland, 1961b, p. 742.

Wald, G.: The distribution and evolution of visual systems. In *Comparative Biochemistry.* New York, Academic Press, 1960, Vol. I, p. 311.

Wald, G.: The photoreceptor process in vision. In *Handbook of Physiology*. I. *Neurophysiology*. Washington, D. C., American Physiological Society, 1959, p. 671.

Wald, G.: The biochemistry of visual excitation. In *Enzymes: Units of Biological Structure and Function*. O.H. Gaebler, ed., New York, Academic Press, 1956, p. 355.

Wald, G.: Photoreceptor process in vision. *Am. J. Ophthal., 40*(5):18, 1955.

Wald, G.: On the mechanism of the visual threshold and visual adaptation. *Science, 119*:887, 1954.

Wald, G.: The biochemistry of vision. *Ann. Rev. Biochem., 22*:497, 1953.

Wald, G.: Biochemical evolution. In *Modern Trends in Physiology and Biochemistry*. New York, Academic Press, 1952.

Wald, G.: Galloxanthin, a carotenoid from the chicken retina. *J. Gen. Physiol., 31*:377, 1948.

Wald, G.: Human vision and the spectrum. *Science, 101*:653, 1945.

Wald, G.: On the distribution of vitamins A_1 and A_2. *J. Gen. Physiol, 22*:391, 1939.

Wald, G.: On rhodopsin in solution. *J. Gen. Physiol., 21*:795, 1938.

Wald, G., and Allen, G.: Fractionation of the eye pigments of *Drosophila melanogaster*. *J. Gen. Physiol., 30*:41, 1946.

Wald, G., Brown, P.K., and Gibbons, I.R.: The problem of visual excitation. *J. Optic. Soc. Am., 53*:20, 1963.

Wald, G., and Brown, P.K.: Human rhodopsin. *Science, 127*:222, 1958.

Wald, G., and Brown, P.K.: The role of sulfhydryl groups in the bleaching and synthesis of rhodopsin. *J. Gen. Physiol., 35*:797, 1952.

Wald, G., and Hubbard, R.: Visual pigment of a decapod crustacean: The lobster. *Nature, 180*:278, 1957.

Wald, G., and Krainin, J.M.: The median eye of *Limulus*: An ultraviolet receptor. *Proc. Nat. Acad. Sc., 50*:1011, 1963.

Wald, G., and Zussman, H.: Carotenoids of the chicken retina. *J. Biol. Chem., 122*:449, 1938.

Wallace, P.M.M.: Ultraviolet microspectrophotometry. In *General Cytochemical Methods*. J.F. Danielli, ed., New York, Academic Press, 1958, Vol. I, p. 163.

Walls, G.L.: *The Vertebrate Eye*. Bloomfield Hills, Michigan, Cranbrook Institute of Science, 1942.

Walther, J.B.: Changes induced in spectral sensitivity and form of retinal action potential of the cockroach eye by selective adaptation. *J. Insect. Physiol., 2*:142, 1958.

Walther, J.B., and Dodt, E.: Die spektralsensitivität von insekten komplexaugen in ultraviolet bis 290 mμ. *Z. Naturforsch., 14B*:273, 1959.

Walther, J.B., and Dodt, E.: Electrophysiologische untersuchongen über die ultraviolettempfind ichkeit von insektenaugen. *Experientia, 13*:333, 1957.

Weale, R.A.: *The Eye and Its Function*. London, Hatton Press, Ltd. 1960, pp. 103-116.

Willmer, E.N.: *Cytology and Evolution*. New York, Academic Press, 1960.

Whipple, H.E. and Hague, E.B., eds.: Photo-neuro-endocrine effects in circadian systems, with particular reference to the eye. *Ann. N.Y. Acad. Sci., 74*:1, 1964.

Wolken, J.J.: The structure and molecular organization of retinal photoreceptors. *J. Optic. Soc. Am., 53*:1, 1963.

Wolken, J.J.: The visual pigments: Absorption spectra of isolated single frog retinal rods and cones. *Invest. Ophthal., 1*:327, 1962a.

Wolken, J.J.: Photoreceptor structures: Their molecular organization for energy transfer, *J. Theoret. Biol., 3*:192, 1962b.

Wolken, J.J.: A structural model for a retinal rod. In *The Structure of the Eye*. G.K. Smelser, ed., New York, Academic Press, 1961a, p. 173.

Wolken, J.J.: The photoreceptor structure. In *International Review of Cytology*, G.H. Bourne and J.F. Danielli, eds., New York, Academic Press, 1961b, p. 173.

Wolken, J.J.: *Euglena: An Experimental Organism for Biochemical and Biophysical Studies*. New Brunswick, New Jersey, Rutgers University Press, 1961c.

Wolken, J.J.: Photoreceptors: Comparative studies. In *Comparative Biochemistry of Photoreactive Systems*. M.B. Allen, ed., New York, Academic Press, 1960a, p. 145.

Wolken, J.J.: The Chloroplast: Its lamellar structure and molecular organization. In *Macromolecular complexes*. M.V. Edds, Jr., ed., New York, Ronald Press, 1960b, p. 85.

Wolken, J.J.: Studies of photoreceptor structures. *Ann. N.Y. Acad. Sc., 74*:164, 1958a.

Wolken, J.J.: Retinal structure, mollusc cephalopods: *Octopus, Sepia. J. Biophys. Biochem. Cytol., 4*:835, 1958b.

Wolken, J.J.: A comparative study of photoreceptors. *Trans. New York Acad. Sc., 19*:315, 1957.

Wolken, J.J.: Photoreceptor structures. I. Pigment monolayers and molecular weight. *J. Cell. Comp. Physiol., 48*:349, 1956a.

Wolken, J.J.: A molecular morphology of Euglena gracilis var bacillaris. J. Protozool., 3:211, 1956b.

Wolken, J.J.: Capenos, J., and Turano, A., Photoreceptor structures. III. Drosophila melanogaster. J. Biophys. and Biochem. Cytol., 3:441, 1957a.

Wolken, J.J., Mellon, A.D., and Contis, G.: Photoreceptor structures. II. Drosophila melanogaster, J. Exp. Zool., 134:383, 1957b.

Wolken, J.J., and Mellon, A.D.: The relationship between chlorophyll and the carotenoids in the algal flagellate, Euglena. J. Gen. Physiol., 39:675, 1956.

Wolken, J.J., Bowness, J.M., and Scheer, I.J.: The visual complex of the insect: Retinene in the housefly. Biochim. et Biophys. Acta, 43:531, 1960.

Wolken, J.J. and Gallik, J.G.: The compound eye of a crustacean: Leptodora kindtii. J. Cell Biol., 26:No. 3, 1965.

Wolken, J.J. and Gross, J.: Development and Characteristics of the Euglena C-type Cytochromes. J. Protozool., 10:189, 1963.

Wolken, J.J., and Gupta, P.D.: Photoreceptor structures of the retinal cells of the cockroach eye. IV. Periplaneta americana and Blaberus giganteus. J. Biophys. and Biochem. Cytol., 9:720, 1961.

Wolken, J.J., and Palade, G.E.: Fine structures of chloroplasts in two flagellates. Ann. N.Y. Acad. Sc., 56:873, 1953.

Wolken, J.J. and Scheer, I.J.: An eye pigment of the cockroach. Exp. Eye Res. 2:182, 1963.

Wolken, J.J., and Shin, E.: Photomotion in Euglena gracilis. I. Photo-kinesis. II. Phototaxis, J. Protozool., 5:39, 1958.

Wolken, J.J., and Strother, G.K.: Microspectrophotometry. Applied Optics, 2:899, 1963.

Wolken, J.J., and Ward, E.N.: Continuous culture of bovine retinal cells. Invest. Ophthal., 1:693, 1962.

Yoshida, M.: Maintenance of visual cells in vitro. Experientia, 16:363, 1960.

Yoshizawa, T., and Wald, G.: Pre-lumirhodopsin and the bleaching of visual pigments. Nature, 197:1279, 1963.

Young, J. Z.: The retina of cephalopods and its degeneration after optic nerve section. Phil. Trans. Roy. Soc. London, S.B., 245:1, 1962.

Young, J. Z.: The optic lobes of Octopus vulgaris. Phil. Trans. Roy. Soc. London, S.B., 245:19, 1962.

Young, J. Z.: Doubt and Certainty in Science. Oxford, England, Oxford University Press, 1960.

Young, T.: *Lectures in Natural Philosophy*. London, W. Savage, 1807, Vol. I., p. 440; Vol. II, pp. 315 and 613.

Young, T.: On the theory of light and colors. *Phil. Trans. Roy. Soc. London*, *92*:12, 1802.

Younger, J.S., Ward, E.N., and Salk, J.W.: Use of color changes of phenol red as the indicator in titrating poliomyelitis viruses or its antibody in a tissue culture system. *Am. J. Hyg.*, *55*:291, 1952.

Zechmeister, L.: Cis-trans isomerization and stereochemistry of carotenoids and diphenylpolyenes. *Chem. Revs.*, *34*:267, 1944.

Zechmeister, L.: *Carotenoids. Cis-Trans Isomeric Carotenoids, Vitamins A, and Arylpolyenes*. New York, Academic Press, 1962.

Zimm, B.M.: Concentrated macromolecular structure. *Revs. Mod. Phys.*, *31*:123, 1959.

Zonnana, H.V.: Fine structure of the *squid* retina. *Bull. Johns Hopkins Hospital*, *109*:180, 1961.

NAME INDEX

SUBJECT INDEX